MW00781463

Refining and Reformulation: the challenge of green motor fuels

ADAM SEYMOUR

EV13
Oxford Institute for Energy Studies
1992

The contents of this paper
are the author's sole responsibility.
They do not necessarily represent the
views of the Oxford Institute for
Energy Studies or any of its Members.

ACKNOWLEDGEMENTS

I would like to thank the many people who have been generous with their time in responding to my many questions and ploughing their way through my first drafts. Most especially I would like to mention Dr Cyrus Tahmassebi and Mike Czesalebe of Ashland Oil , Alan Hegberg of Phillips Petroleum, Phil Trimmer and Mark Townley of BP, Dr John Jefferies of Exxon and (by no means least!) Dr Henry Kruk and Dr Graham Bodwell who are currently employed at the Oxford University organic chemistry laboratories. Needless to say they bear no responsibility for the final state of the text.

CONTENTS

TABLES

ABBREVIATIONS

1. Legislative terminology

AQCR	Air Quality Control Region
BG	Baseline Gasoline
CAA	Clean Air Act
CAAA	Clean Air Act Amendments
EPA	Environmental Protection Agency
HAP	Hazardous Air Pollutant
HC	Hydrocarbon
MACT	Maximum Available Control Technology
NAAQS	National Ambient Air Quality Standards
NMOG	Non-Methane Organic Gas
SIP	State Implementation Plan
VOC	Volatile Organic Compound

2. Refinery and Oil Industry Terminology

CRU	Catalytic Reforming Unit
FCCU	Fluid Catalytic Cracking Unit
HF	Hydrofluoric Acid
mb/d	Million Barrels Per Day
MON	Motor Octane Number
R&D	Research And Development
RON	Research Octane Number
RVP	Reid Volatility Pressure

3. Chemical Terminology

CO	Carbon Monoxide
ETBE	Ethyl-Tertiary-Butylether
MTBE	Methyl-Tertiary-Butylether
NO_2	Nitrogen Dioxide
NO_3	Nitrate Anion
NOx	Nitrogen Oxides
HNO_3	Nitric Acid
OH	Hydroxyl Radical
PM	Particulate Matter
ppm	Parts Per Million
SO_2	Sulphur Dioxide
SO_4	Sulphate Anion
SOx	Sulphur Oxides
H_2SO_4	Sulphuric Acid
TAME	Tertiary-Amylmethylether

GLOSSARY

1. Legislative Terminology

Air quality control region: The Clean Air Act divides the USA into regions which display similar metereological conditions, known as air quality control regions, for the purpose of monitoring and regulating air quality.

Emissions control diagnostic system: An emissions control diagnostic system must, at least, include an oxygen sensor, to minimize CO emissions, and a catalytic converter. The system should also be able to monitor the age and performance of emissions-related systems within the vehicle.

Hazardous air pollutants: Substances may be listed as HAPs if they are known to be 'carcinogenic, mutagenic, teratogenic, neurotoxic, which cause reproductive dysfunction, or which are acutely or chronically toxic'.[1]

National ambient air quality standard: Six pollutants namely particulates under 10 microns in diameter, ozone, lead, sulphur dioxide, nitrogen dioxide and carbon monoxide, have each been assigned a standard, known as the National Ambient Air Quality Standards (NAAQS), involving a one-hourly, eight-hourly or twenty four-hourly air concentration mean.

Nonattainment: An area is deemed nonattainment if its monitored air quality violates any one of the six NAAQS more than once a year, or, in the case of ozone, three times in each three-year period.

Stage I recovery system: Stage I systems are carbon canisters fitted to the entrance of the petrol tank. The systems recovers hydrocarbon vapours during refuelling and running of the vehicle.

Stage II recovery system: Stage II systems recover the evaporative losses during refuelling and return the hydrocarbon vapours to the petrol station.

Toxic air pollutant: The term 'toxic air pollutants' means aggregate emissions of benzene, 1,3-butadiene, polycyclic organic matter, acetaldehyde and formaldehyde.

Volatile organic compound: Volatile organic compound is a generic term describing hydrocarbons and hydrocarbon derivatives. In this study we are concerned with automotive VOC emissions and their propensity to photochemically react with NOx to form ground-level ozone.

2. Refinery and Motor Car Fuel Terminology

Alkylation: Alkylation is a type of chemical transformation. In oil refineries it is used to convert light olefins to branched-chain molecules which have higher performance in gasoline engines. Common catalysts used in the alkylation process include sulphuric and hydrofluoric acids.

Aromatics: A class of organic compounds, related to hydrocarbons, with a closed system of pi electrons. Aromatics serve to raise the octane quality of gasoline.

Capacity creep: A term coined by consultants Purvin and Gertz which has gained widespread acceptance. Describes the ability of refiners to increase the nameplate capacity of a process over time through the use of technical resouces aimed at optimal integration of the process within the individual refinery.

Captive processes: that is a process located within a refinery.

Catalyst: a substance which has the effect of promoting a chemical reaction without its own composition being altered.

Catalytic Reforming: In this refinery process paraffins are converted to isoparaffins and naphthenes and naphthenes are converted to other aromatics. These chemical transformations improve the performance of the straight-run naphtha feed in gasoline engines.

Cetane: The cetane index measures the ignition performance of diesel. Like the octane number for gasoline the cetane index is the prime indicator of diesel quality.

Cracking: Cracking is a refiner process which breaks hydrocarbon molecules up into smaller and lighter molecules, thereby, increasing the yield of higher-value light hydrocarbon streams, such as gasoline, per barrel of crude oil.

Desulphurization: There are many types of desulphurization processes. Hydrotreating is a process by which cracked products (ie. heavy hydrocarbon compounds that are broken down into smaller and lighter ones) are stabilized and impurities, such as trace metals and sulphur, are removed by reacting them with hydrogen. In the reaction sulphur is turned to hydrogen sulphide gas which is then fed into a sulphur recovery unit. The elemental sulphur is marketed and the hydrogen is recycled. *Hydroprocessing* is applied to the combination of hydrocracking and hydrotreating. *Hydrodesulphurization* is used to describe a process whose prime function is removing sulphur. All these terms are in many ways interchangeable as the processes are simultaneous within the refinery configuration.

Gasoline volatility: Gasoline volatility, which is measured in terms of Reid Vapour Pressure (RVP), must be sufficiently low so that the fuel remains liquid in the petrol tank and sufficiently high that the liquid evaporates in the carburettor. Therefore the RVP of gasoline must be lower in the summer than the winter.

Isomerization: Two main types of isomerization process are found in oil refineries. The first converts butane to isobutane and is used to supplement the feed for the alkylation unit. This is known as C4 isomerization. The second is used to convert pentanes and hexanes, supplied in the straight-run gasoline feed, to isomers which have a higher octane number and, so, perform better in gasoline engines. This is known as C5/C6 isomerization.

Octane number: 'The octane number of gasoline is a measure of its propensity to ignite under compression. The higher the octane number the less flammable a gasoline is. As the gasoline engine relies on a spark plug to ignite the petrol fumes in the compression chamber the less flammable the gasoline the better the engine performs.'[2]

Oxygenate: an oil industry term employed to describe a blending component capable of rapidly increasing the oxygen content of motor car fuels, such as ethers or alcohols.

Refinery complexity: In this study the complexity of a refinery refers to the degree of process options available to a refiner according to the refinery process configuration.

Reid Vapour Pressure: RVP is a measure of gasoline's propensity to evaporate at standard temperature and pressure.

1   The Clean Air Act Amendments, 1990, Title III, Section 301 (b)(2).
2   A. Seymour, *The World Refining System and Oil Products Trade*, OIES 1990, p.4.

1   INTRODUCTION

The subject of environmental legislation and its impact on the oil industry is a very large one. In this study I shall focus only on the question of the future impacts of reformulated motor car fuels mandated in the 1990 amendments to the Clean Air Act (CAA) on the US refining industry.

The US refining industry is subject to a wide variety of environmental controls. Acid rain provisions require total refinery emissions of SOx and NOx to be reduced. In ozone nonattainment areas the CAA requires monitoring and control technologies for volatile organic compounds (VOCs) emissions. The handling and disposal of many hazardous substances used in refining are also strictly regulated. However, over the past ten years it has been the reformulation of petroleum products, such as gasoline and diesel, that has attracted the most attention. This is because product reformulation not only necessitates fundamental change in technology and process operations but also affects the refiner's ability to recoup costs, which include all costs incurred as a result of environmental regulation. The automotive fuels are particularly crucial to American refiners as their production and marketing have proved to be profitable.

The United States is the single largest consumer of crude oil and oil products in the world. Any change in the behaviour of American industry brought about as a result of pollution regulation could, therefore, have implications for both the world oil market and the global environment. US environmental regulations have another international significance because of the propensity of other OECD countries to follow suit, especially with regard to the control of motor car pollution.

The 1990 Clean Air Act Amendments (CAAA) enacted on 15 November 1990 will involve a substantial increase in the commitment of financial resources to the environment by American industry as they attempt to tackle the problems of urban pollution, acid rain and hazardous air pollutants (HAPs). One of the most conservative estimates, made by the Bush Administration, projects the total costs of the 1990 CAAA at $11 billion in 1995 rising to between $22 and $25 billion in 2005, compared with current expenditures of $32 billion on pollution control. The reformulation of motor car fuels constitutes a significant part of these cost projections, and has a central role in Congress's attempt to combat both urban pollution and HAPs.

Within the oil industry, processing, and refining in particular, will bear a significant proportion of costs incurred as a result of the 1990 CAAA. For the first time since 1971 the oil industry's 1991 budget for capital outlays in the US downstream sector is higher than for the upstream. Over 50 per cent of the budgeted increase in downstream expenditure is for refining and has been made necessary as a result of the 1990 CAAA's provisions. In global terms 'current estimates of $200 to $300 billion of refining investment over ten years are potentially greater than that required by OPEC to invest in crude supply over the same period.'[1]

For all these reasons the reformulation of motor car fuels and its impact on the US refining industry provides a focus of concern for the oil industry and environmentalists the world over.

After the introduction, this study is divided into four main parts. Chapter 2 describes the exact terms of the motor car fuel regulations contained in the 1990 CAAA and explains the context for Congress's approach as well as looking at the difficulties that meeting these regulations may cause refiners.

Chapter 3 assesses the significance of uncertainties and

---

1   Mark Townley and Ronald Spiers of BP's Industry and Margin Analysis team, 'Challenges facing refiners', *Oxford Energy Forum*, OIES August 1991, Issue 6.

ambiguities which affect the objectives and stipulations of the legislation and those that surround the possible modes of implementation. Chapter 4 examines the technological cost of supplying new motor fuels whilst assuming away the significant uncertainties that are inherent in the legislation. Because of the various problems Congress has had in the past with similar attempts at tackling motor car pollution, not least with the phasing out of lead in gasoline, the legislation governing the new green motor fuels is very complex and will be finalized in various stages over a long period, through to the next century. Therefore, many assumptions about the outcome of these crucial stages must be made in any analysis of the technological demands and costs of these regulations.

In Chapter 5 the results of the previous two chapters are brought together in considering the impact of the legislation on the structure and behaviour of the refining industry in the United States.

Descriptions of the health impact of motor car emissions and of the legislative history of the CAA have been included as Annexes 1 and 2, respectively, for all those readers not acquainted with these backgrounds.

This study is a survey of wide-ranging issues arising from the introduction of the CAAA in the United States. It brings together in a coherent framework material which is dispersed in specialist journals across three areas of investigation, namely the oil industry, the environment and the legal system. As such it provides a synthetic reference on the legislation, its possible interpretations and more importantly on its likely economic impacts on costs, investment and structure of the refining industry and on the pattern of motor fuel trade. This study, however, goes further than the literature in assessing the estimates of implementation costs facing refiners and, more particularly, the assumptions that lie behind those estimates. It focuses on the uncertainties which surround the legislation and for the first time presents an in-depth and independent analysis of the possible impacts of investment. Finally, it brings explicitly both the political dimensions of the evolving issues which the legislation and its implementation raise and the geographical regional implications of the 1990 CAAA's impact on motor fuel markets and trade.

Two methodological remarks need to be made from the outset. First, when analysing in this study the impact of legislation on the structure of US refining as a whole it would be easy to lose sight of the great diversity of refining interests and markets in that country. This could lead to a serious understatement of the short-run constraints faced by refiners, and of the existence of many distinct areas unconnected by pipeline. This feature is important because it limits cross-blending opportunities that would otherwise be available to refiners. For analytical convenience analysts are often forced to aggregate refining operations and product supply as if the plants in a country or region could be treated as a single refinery.

Secondly, possible supply constraints in the long run are also difficult to evaluate due to the approximate nature of refinery process capacity figures. The capacity of a process may increase over time as a result of refiner experience in, for instance, 'debottlenecking' or 'revamping' processes, thereby successfully integrating process operations within that individual refinery configuration.[2] The opportunity for 'capacity creep'[3], as this phenomenon is generally known, is especially marked when new demands are placed on a process, for instance as a result of environmental regulations. This phenomenon may also be reversed if a process becomes less crucial to refiner operations. In this case technical resources may be diverted to other processes within the refinery resulting

---

2   Quite simply, optimization relies on knowing your 'pipes'; see A. J. Suchanek, 'Refiners must fit chemistry to the pipes', *Oil and Gas Journal,* 17 December 1984, pp.115–7.

3   A term coined by consultants Purvin and Gertz which has gained widespread acceptance. Capacity creep was evidenced in the USA between 1985 and 1989 when despite pressure on octane (exerted both by lead phaseout and demand for better performance fuels), restrictions on volatility and little investment in additional octane-enhancing capacity US refiners were able to increase gasoline supplies by 8 per cent from 6.4 mb/d to 6.9 mb/d.

in deterioration of process yields. Other technological advances in, for instance, catalysts and blending systems may also aid the flexibility of refiners' responses to environmental demands.

2   THE CLEAN AIR ACT AND MOTOR FUELS

2.1   Introduction

In framing the 1990 CAAA, Congress has attempted to reflect the scale and focus of American concern. Since 1981 there has been sporadic, though sometimes very intense, lobbying to amend the CAA. The 1984 disaster at a chemical facility in Bhopal, a similar incident in West Virginia in the following year, the freak ozone season in the summer of 1988 and the continuing devastation caused by acid rain combined with increased fears over the unhealthful acid aerosols[1] all played their respective parts in prioritizing the problems of hazardous air pollutants, urban pollution and sulphur oxide emissions. In this context the issue of human health has clearly been prioritized ahead of other environmental concerns such as global warming.

The health impact of vehicle emissions has been a focus of US legislation since 1965 although more emphatically during the last ten years (see Annex 1). However, the much publicized measures, such as the phasing out of lead additives and mandatory catalytic converters, have not solved the problem. The predominant image of Los Angeles, where the strictest legislation in the world is in force, remains the rush-hour traffic and the fumes that mar the sunny surroundings.

Three means have been employed by Congress to reduce vehicle pollution. The most popular is the specification of

---

1   'Acid aerosol' is a term used to describe acidic liquids, usually nitric or sulphuric, suspended in the ambient air. Further, this fine spray can become more unhealthful as it may contain dissolved airborne metal particles, such as lead or aluminium. See also Annex 1.

increasingly stringent tailpipe standards for new vehicles. The drawback of this approach is that it is a long-term policy that can only have effects when old vehicles are replaced by new ones. The second involves altering the composition of fuel which can have a more immediate impact on vehicle emissions. The third, and least politically popular, has been to restrict traffic. The concern over vehicle emissions is such that the 1990 Clean Air Act Amendments (CAAA) has employed all three means (see Annex 2).

The purpose of this chapter is to describe the legislation governing product reformulation and to place it in context.

2.2 The 1980s: The Vanishing Miracle

The impact of road transport emissions is particularly diverse and difficult to combat (see Table 1). Pollution from road transport is not restricted to the visible smoke from an automobile's tailpipe. The evaporative losses that occur in the refining, distribution and marketing of gasoline and diesel also have bad environmental consequences. Furthermore, emissions from fuel evaporation and combustion have indirect effects on human health as they remain in the atmosphere and react to form other environmental hazards, such as ozone. These pollutants act as precursors to environmental hazards such as acid deposition and ground-level ozone formation. The indirect nature of this impact poses problems for environmental regulation, as does the very seasonal nature of pollutants, such as ozone and CO.

When first presented in the 1970s the three-way catalytic converter was seen to be the technical answer to this environmental problem: an appliance that could conceivably be fitted to every car and cut out 90 per cent of urban pollutants. The only precondition for such a move to become technically feasible was the reformulation of automotive fuels since the catalysts are intolerant of lead in gasoline and sulphur in diesel. The pressure for reformulation was further strengthened by the acid rain lobby, and the much publicized detrimental effects of lead on mental development. The only

Table 1: Vehicle Emissions and the Environment

Vehicle Emission	Gasoline's vs. Diesel's contribution to emissions *	Environmental Impact	Secondary Reaction	Environmental Impact
Carbon Monoxide	Gasoline combustion less complete. More carbon monoxide.	Impairs blood's ability to absorb oxygen.	Carbon Dioxide	Contributes to global warming.
Carbon Dioxide	Diesel combustion more complete. More carbon dioxide.	Contributes to global warming.		
Unburned VOCs	Greater evaporation from gasoline.	Inhalation may cause cancer, reproductive problems, neuro-toxicity or chronic organ toxicity. Benzene, 1,3-butadiene and POM have been identified as the most toxic VOC emissions from vehicles.	Ground-level ozone (VOCs react with NOx in the presence of sunlight).	Inhalation causes lung and eye irritation and damage to immune system. Ozone cuts visibility and contributes to global warming. Ozone deposition damages crops.
Exhaust VOCs (also particulates)	Diesel contains larger compounds and, so, is less combustible.			
Particulates (includes exhaust VOCs, acidic salts and soot)	Diesel emits 30 to 100 times more particles than a catalyst-equipped gasoline engine.	Particulates damage the lungs and may carry other hazardous substance on their surface. See VOCs and acid salts.		

Table 1 (cont)

Vehicle Emission	Gasoline's vs. Diesel's	Environmental Impact	Secondary Reaction	Environmental Impact	Tertiary Reaction	Environmental Impact
NOx (1)	Diesel engines have better combustion and lower ignition temperatures and, so, should emit fewer NOx.	Of the NOx nitrogen dioxide is the most directly harmful. Inhalation causes or aggravates respiratory disorders. Also damages vegetation and reduces visibility due to its brown colour.	Nitric acid.	Inhalation of nitric acid droplets will cause severe damage to lung tissue. Deposition or acid rain, causes damage to vegetation and aquatic life and frees metals into the food and water supply. Also corrodes buildings.	Nitrates.	Inhalation causes respiratory problems. Also suspended particles decrease visibility (see particulates).
NOx (2)			Ozone.	See page above.		
Sulphur Dioxide	In the USA, diesel contains 90 times more sulphur than gasoline.	Similar effects to nitrogen dioxide although sulphur dioxide is more acidic and, so, more unhealthful.	Sulphuric acid.	More acidic than its nitrogen-based counterpart. Also vegetation is much less tolerant of sulphur compounds.	Sulphates.	More acidic than its nitrogen-based counterpart.

* Available emission control technology not taken into account unless specifically stated.

Key: VOCs = Volatile organic compounds, NOx = Nitrogen oxides.

Sources: see Annex 1

obstacle was the cost of reformulation to both industry and consumers.

During the 1980s it was generally realized that the catalytic converter was not a miracle cure as many had previously thought. The number of vehicles, vehicle miles travelled and the proportion of diesel engines in the US fleet (which cannot be fitted with catalytic converters at current diesel fuel sulphur levels) all increased. Also, stringent tailpipe standards raised the price of new vehicles thereby adding incentives for owners not to replace their old high-polluting vehicles.

Furthermore it soon became apparent that the phasing out of lead had environmental trade-offs not foreseen in the legislation. The most economic approach for refiners to maintain gasoline quality in the face of the removal of lead was to increase the gasoline concentration of butane and aromatic compounds. However, aromatic compounds, such as benzene, are also carcinogenic and the additional use of butane increased gasoline volatility. In this way lead removal resulted in decreased airborne lead concentration but increased emissions of carcinogenic and ozone-precursor hydrocarbons (see Table 1).

The reformulation of gasoline was no longer considered a means to an end but an end in itself. Public concern over summer ozone levels and 'cancer alleys'[2] has refocused the debate on the intrinsic qualities of gasoline and the environmental trade-offs that resulted from phasing out lead. In 1989, after considerable pressure from state legislatures, a limit of 9 Reid Vapour Pressure (RVP) was federally mandated for summertime gasoline. This subtle policy shift was the prelude to further reformulations in 1990, and was indicative of the growing public perception of hydrocarbon fuels being environmentally harmful products.

---

2   'The levels of toxic air pollutants continue to climb in such notorious "cancer alleys" as those between Baton Rouge and New Orleans and Beaumont and Galveston.' G. J. MacDonald, 'This common inheritance – an American view' in *Energy & Environment*, vol.2 no.2 1991, p.133.

2.3 The 1990s: A Failsafe Approach?

In the 1990 CAAA (see Annex 2) Congress introduced new specifications for gasoline and diesel supplies, and mandated three new fuels: reformulated gasoline, oxygenated gasoline and clean alternative fuel. However, the 1990 CAAA provisions governing reformulated and oxygenated gasolines were left open-ended pending further research into the impact of gasoline components on vehicle emissions and negotiations between the oil industry and the EPA over the means of implementation. The results of the regulatory negotiations or 'Reg-Neg' process will be finalized on 15 November 1991. Preliminary agreement between the two parties was reached on 16 August 1991 and an analysis of the agreement is included here. The Auto/Oil Air Quality Improvement Research Programme was started by major oil companies and car manufacturers in late 1989 and will continue through to 1993. The conclusions of the programme are being and will continue to be used by the EPA to determine the specifications for green gasolines and to create models whereby various gasoline formulations may be certified.

The reformulation of motor fuel supplies form a small part of Congress's plan to improve US air quality in the 1990s. For refiners to fulfil these requirements they must know the 'what?', the 'when?' and the 'where?' (see Table 2 for summarized results).

The diesel mandate is clear.[3] As of 1 October 1993 diesel sold at US service stations, must have a maximum of 0.05 (wt.) per cent sulphur content and a minimum of 40 on the cetane index. The regulation affects 1.38 mb/d of diesel supplies, or around 46 per cent of the total US distillate market, which will now have to be separated from the rest of the US distillate supplies.[4]

The mandate for US gasoline supplies is less clear. As of 1 January 1995 all gasoline supplies must 'contain additives to prevent the accumulation of deposits in engines or fuel

---

3   The Clean Air Act Amendments, 1990, Section 217(i).

Table 2: Implementation Schedule and Specifications for Automotive Fuels.

Fuel Type	*What?*
US Gasoline	All gasolines must contain a 'EPA approved' detergent to reduce engine deposits.
Reformulated Gasoline	Reformulated GasolinePhase I: In order to be certified as phase one reformulated gasoline it must contain 1 (vol.)% benzene max., 2 (wt.)% oxygen min. (BUT no greater than 2.7 (wt.)% MTBE or 2.1 (wt.)% of any other oxygenate unless the refiner can demonstrate that higher concentrations will not result in increased NOx emissions) and summertime volatility must be limited to 7.2 or 8.1 psi depending on the area. In addition the oxygen, benzene and aromatics contents must be such that the fuel achieves a 15% reduction in annual toxic emissions according to a 'simple' model. In 1997 phase one reformulated gasolines must be recertified through a more complex model. Phase II: A fuel formulation will be certified as a phase two reformulated gasoline if, according to the complex model, it achieves a minimum reduction of 20% both in summertime VOC and annual toxic emissions.
Oxygenated Gasoline	Phase I: 2.7 (wt.)% oxygen min. for four winter months min. Phase II: 3.1 (wt.)% oxygen min. for four winter months min.
Clean Fuel	Clean fuel may be any fuel that when used in a clean fuel vehicle 'complies with the standards and requirements applicable to such vehicle'. The vehicle standards establish emission requirements for CO, NOx, NMOG and PM after 50,000 and 100,000 miles.
Ref. Diesel	0.05 (wt.)% sulphur max., 40 cetane index min.

Source: The 1990 Clean Air Act Amendments.

Table 2: Implementation Schedule and Specifications for Automotive Fuels.

When?	*Where?*
By 1 January 1995	Nationwide
Phase I: 1 January 1995	Phase I & II: The 9 worst ozone nonattainment cities with an opt-in clause for all other ozone non-attainment areas.
Phase II: 1 January 2000	
Phase I: 1 November 1992	Phase I: All CO nonattainment areas.
Phase II: 1 November 2001	Phase II: All serious CO nonattainment areas.
Phase I: 1996–8	Phase I: California and the 9 worst ozone nonattainment cities will require supporting clean fuel retail outlets
Phase II: 1998	Phase II: 9 worst ozone nonattainment cities. This will not require retail clean fuel outlets.
1 October 1993.	Nationwide.

systems'.[5] Congress has directed the Environmental Protection Agency (EPA)[6] to determine the specifications for such additive(s) by 15 November 1992. Only then will refiners have a precise idea of the changes and, therefore, the costs involved.

For oxygenated gasoline only the 'what?' and the 'where?' have been defined by Congress.[7] Gasoline containing a minimum 2.7 (wt.) per cent oxygen must be made available in all CO nonattainment areas which have 'a carbon monoxide design value of 9.5 ppm[8] or above'. These areas were designated in the first half of 1991 and include forty cities which currently consume between 27 and 40 per cent[9] of US gasoline supplies (for the purpose of our analysis we have used a 30 per cent projection). Gasoline containing a minimum 3.1 (wt.) per cent oxygen will be made available in areas that have not attained the CO National Ambient Air Quality Standards (NAAQS) by 31 December 2000. The 'what?' is slightly complicated by the 1990 CAAA provision for tradeable oxygen credits within a nonattainment area. This means that some fuel suppliers may buy oxygen credits, if available, in order to market a gasoline with less than the required oxygen content.

The 'when?' of oxygenated gasoline is not fixed. Gasoline with an oxygen content of 2.7 (wt.) per cent should be made

---

4   Energy Information Administration, 'Fuel Oil and Kerosene Sales 1989', DOE/EIA–0535 (89), (Washington DC January 1991), p.3 cited in L. Shyu, A. Bohn, 'Effects of the Clean Air Act's highway diesel fuel oil provisions', *Petroleum Supply Monthly*, Energy Information Administration June 1991.

5   The Clean Air Act Amendments, 1990, Title II, Section 219(l).

6   The EPA is responsible to Congress for the administration of the CAA.

7   The Clean Air Act Amendments, 1990, Title II, Section 219(m).

8   Strictly speaking an area could be designated CO nonattainment, ie. 9.1 ppm or above, and yet not be required to use oxygenated gasoline.

9   27 per cent from G. H. Unzelman, 'U.S. Clean Air Act expands role for oxygenates', *Oil and Gas Journal*, 15 April 1991 p.44 and 40 per cent from Scherr et al, 'Clean Air Act complicates refinery planning', *Oil and Gas Journal*, 27 May 1991 pp.68–75.

available in the winter of 1992 and that of the higher oxygen content in the winter of 2001. The relevant length of winter will vary from state to state; however, the CAAA provides that it must be at least four months long and must start by 1 November.

However, the EPA has the option of delaying start-up in an area for up to two years if (a) use of oxygenated gasoline in that area would cause the failure of that area to attain any NAAQS other than that for CO; (b) use of oxygenated gasoline in that area would not contribute to the attainment of the NAAQS for CO; or (c) there is insufficient production or distribution capacity to supply the area's gasoline demand. The last clause is most likely to result in waivers especially as the EPA have determined that oxygenate supply currently being consumed in attainment areas may not be diverted.[10]

In the case of reformulated gasoline, its content remains unspecified because it is defined by Congress in terms of the emission reductions it must achieve relative to 'baseline' gasoline.[11] Phase one reformulated gasoline must achieve a 15 per cent reduction both in VOC emissions during the summer months, and toxic emissions over the year as a whole. Also the use of reformulated gasoline should not result in increased NOx emissions. By 2000 Congress have mandated the production and supply of phase two reformulated gasoline to replace its predecessor in ozone nonattainment areas. Phase two will have to achieve no less than a further 20 per cent reduction in both summertime VOC and annual toxic emissions.

As mentioned before, the specifications for and method of certifying reformulated gasoline were not finalized in the 1990 CAAA. Congress proposed that some specifications, namely 2 per cent minimum oxygen content by weight and maximums of

---

10   John R. Hall, chairman and chief executive officer of Ashland Oil Inc. cited in 'GM mounts push for reformulated motor fuel now', *Oil and Gas Journal*, 25 March 1991 p.28.

11   339 sulphur ppm, 1.53 (vol.)% benzene, 8.7 RVP, 87.3 Octane (RON + MON)/2, 32 (vol.)% aromatics and 9.2 (vol.)% olefins.

both 1 per cent benzene and 25 per cent aromatics contents by volume, should be adopted if they were found by the Auto/Oil programme to achieve the 15 per cent reductions in summertime VOC emissions and annual toxic emissions and, also, not to increase NOx emissions. In addition Congress allowed that other fuel formulations could be certified as reformulated gasoline if they were shown to achieve 'equivalent or greater reductions in emissions of ozone forming volatile organic compounds and emissions of toxic air pollutants'.[12]

Gasoline produced by refineries for ozone nonattainment areas after 1 January 1995 will be certified as phase one reformulated gasoline by the EPA if the fuel formulation is shown, through a combination of testing and the appropriate Auto/Oil programme model, to conform to certain specifications and to achieve the mandated reductions in summertime VOC and toxic emissions. In essence the specifications for phase one reformulated gasoline (see Table 2 for full details) include a minimum oxygen content, reduction in the maximum volatility of summertime gasoline, a maximum benzene content and an implied maximum[13] for aromatics content. In 1995 and 1996 the EPA will use a 'simple' model to certify phase one reformulated gasoline as achieving the emissions reductions. However, in 1997 and beyond refiners will have to 'recertify' their gasolines through the use of a more 'complex' model which will include a greater number of fuel parameters. Phase two reformulated gasolines will be certified for production in 2000 using the complex model.

Reformulated fuel has been mandated for the nine worst nonattainment cities. However, 88 other ozone nonattainment areas are also allowed to 'opt-in' in the case of the reformulated fuel programme. This means that the demand for reformulated

---

12   The Clean Air Act Amendments, 1990, Title II, Section 219(k)(4).

13   The aromatic content of the gasoline, along with benzene and oxygen contents, will be the variables that will determine the results of the Auto/Oil programme's model as to the reduction in toxic emissions. The higher the aromatic content the higher the toxic emissions.

gasoline could be anywhere between 22 and 55 per cent of total US gasoline supplies depending on how many areas 'opt-in'.[14] It is likely that many states will decide whether to opt-in or not in November 1993 when they are due to submit their plans, known as the State Implementation Plan (SIPs), detailing state emission reductions in accordance with the terms of the 1990 CAAA.[15]

A waiver clause, identical to that applied to the oxygenated fuel programme, has been included in the reformulated fuel programme. The initial date is 1 January 1995 for phase one and 1 January 2000 for phase two. If the EPA determines that there is insufficient reformulated gasoline production capacity to supply the demand of the area then the EPA may waiver the mandate for up to three years.

In the 1990 CAAA, Congress has also attempted to prevent the sort of environmental trade-offs that resulted from the removal of lead from gasoline. Of most concern to Congress was that aromatic-rich gasoline blending components would simply be shifted from the regulated to the unregulated products or areas. In the 1990 CAAA Congress has mandated that these aromatics cannot be 'dumped' into gasoline supplies destined for ozone attainment areas or road diesel[16] supplies. Also the average sulphur and olefin contents and distillation range for gasoline in 1990 will be established as the maximums allowable for reformulated gasoline.

The 1990 CAAA provisions for a clean fuel programme contain similar uncertainties to that of the reformulated gasoline programme. The composition of clean fuel is defined by the tailpipe standards for clean fuel vehicles, that is 'any

---

14 For the 22 per cent see Unzelman, op.cit, and for the upper limit see Scherr et al, op.cit.

15 Ibid.

16 As the cetane quality of diesel is adversely affected by the inclusion of aromatics, unlike gasoline quality, the establishment of a minimum cetane index will curtail refiners' options. A minimum cetane index of 40 roughly correlates to a maximum aromatics content of 35 (vol.) per cent see L. Shyu, A. Bohn, op.cit.

fuel...or power source (including electricity) used in a clean-fuel vehicle that complies with the standards and requirements applicable to such vehicle'.[17] Determining the composition of clean fuel will, therefore, require the coordination of car manufacturers and fuel suppliers.

Two types of clean fuel programme are set out in the 1990 CAAA. The first is the pilot test programme mandated for California and starting in 1996. This requires 'that clean alternative fuels be made available and offered for sale at an adequate number of locations with sufficient geographic distribution to ensure convenient refueling'.[18] Other serious, severe or extreme ozone nonattainment areas may 'opt-in' giving only a one year notice to vehicle manufacturers and fuels suppliers. Opting-in does not imply a mandate but it does enable the nonattainment areas to provide three incentives with which to encourage the establishment of a programme. The first involves a 'registration fee on new motor vehicles...which are not clean-fuel vehicles in the amount of at least 1 percent of the cost of the vehicle'.[19] The second allows clean-fuel vehicles to be exempt from traffic control measures, and the third allows preferential use of parking spaces by clean-fuel vehicles.

The second clean fuel programme involves only centrally fuelled vehicle fleets in ozone (serious, severe or extreme) or CO (serious) nonattainment cities (defined as over 250,000 population in 1980). Fleets of ten or more vehicles operated by a single person must begin to buy clean-fuel vehicles if they wish to expand or start anew in 1998 and beyond. The proportion of clean-fuel vehicles that fleet operators will need to purchase will be phased in over several years. Fuel suppliers must 'make clean alternative fuel available to covered fleet operators at locations at which covered fleet vehicles are centrally fuelled'.[20]

---

17   The Clean Air Act Amendments, 1990, Title II, Section 241.
18   Ibid, Section 249(2).
19   Ibid.
20   Ibid, Section 246.

2.4   Conclusion

The 1990 CAAA constitutes Congress's most determined attempt yet to solve the problem of urban pollution caused by traffic. In the short to medium term Congress has mandated new fuel specifications, enhanced vehicle inspections, stage II recovery nozzles at petrol stations, increased vehicle inspection programmes and traffic control measures if emission reduction targets for ozone nonattainment areas are not met. With a long-term view to replacing the US vehicle fleet Congress has set increasingly stringent tailpipe emission specifications for vehicle manufacturers aimed at reducing hydrocarbon emissions by 39 per cent and nitrogen oxide emissions by 60 per cent. Congress has also introduced advanced emission control diagnostic systems, 'cold start' emission specifications and stage I recovery for new cars. With an even greater time-span in mind the CAAA has provided a base from which the USA could make the transition from a hydrocarbon to a clean-fuel vehicle fleet.

Unwittingly, however, Congress has sent a very mixed message to refiners. On the one hand, it proposes a reformulation of the automotive fuels that will require considerable investment. On the other hand, this progressive form of legislation has not provided the clear mandate that refiners need to make that investment.

What is clear from the 1990 CAAA is that Congress mistrusts the intentions of the refining industry and is holding a very big stick to threaten it with. From Congress's perspective the environmental trade-off involved with replacing lead in gasoline was purely the result of refiners' economic self-interest and lack of social conscience rather than the product of misguided legislation. The stick brandished by Congress is of course the threat to move away from hydrocarbon fuel. As a result of reformulated and oxygenated gasolines, about 8 per cent of US gasoline supplies will be ether or alcohol by 1995–8. Further the Californian pilot test programme for clean-fuel vehicles will commence in 1996, just a few years from now. In the past, environmental initiatives started in California have tended to spread to the rest of the USA and beyond.[21]

---

21   There are signs that Japanese gasoline may soon be oxygenated, see *Petroleum Argus*, 15 July 1991 p.8.

3 UNCERTAINTIES SURROUNDING THE LEGISLATION AND THE DECISION TO INVEST

3.1 Introduction

The Clean Air Act is only one of the many that attempt to prevent the contamination of the environment. However, ambient air must be the most difficult medium to clean through the use of policy regulation. In comparing air and water Senator Symms notes that 'regulated entities under the water act are functionally operating within plant-wide 'bubbles' whereas air cannot be so easily funnelled into one regulated waste stream'.[1] This fact makes it difficult both to monitor air quality and to understand the behaviour of emissions in the ambient air and, therefore, to control air quality through the regulation of emissions. For this reason provisions in the 1990 CAAA for monitoring the environmental programmes and estimating their benefit are complex and involve a good deal of bureaucracy and expense.

Other complexities surrounding new motor car fuel regulations are the result of Congress's attempt to find a cost-effective approach to cleaning urban air. The cost of reformulating the entire US gasoline supply would be very large. Such expenditure would also be wasteful as large areas of the USA, especially in Middle America, have no problem with CO or ozone. However, by only mandating supply of green gasoline for specific metropolitan areas much stress will be created in the distribution system which has not evolved to cope with such boundaries. This area-by-area approach to the

---

1   *Senate Report No. 101–228*, 'Clean Air Act Amendments', 27 October 1990, p.488.

introduction of 'green' products also raises the problem of how to prevent pollution being relocated rather than reduced on a nationwide basis.

The complexity of the problem and of the approaches to its remedy is naturally associated with considerable uncertainties about the precise interpretation of parts of the legislation and about future modes of implementation. Four types of uncertainty are revealed by an analysis of the 1990 CAAA. They relate to: (1) the environmental objectives of new motor fuel legislation, (2) the terms of the new motor car fuel legislation themselves, (3) the other provisions of the 1990 CAA which overlap with the new motor car fuel legislation, and (4) the administration of the new motor fuel legislation. In this chapter the considerable uncertainties inherent in the terms, administration and implementation of the motor car fuel regulations are described and evaluated.

3.2   Uncertainties Relating to the Environmental Objectives of the Legislation

The replacement of lead by increased aromatics in gasoline has shown that environmental regulation can have unforeseen consequences and that environmental policy may be reversed if the concern of the American public swings in another direction. This has serious implications for refiners' investment strategy over the long term. Refiners, however, who invested in Catalytic Reforming Units (CRU) during the 1980s in order to replace lead in gasoline will now have to face the problem of disinvesting in CRU capacity during the 1990s as a result of current aromatics restrictions (see section 4.2).

The primary concern over the environmental benefits of new automotive fuels is that the proposed oxygen and aromatics specifications for reformulated gasoline will have no impact on the problem of ground-level ozone formation. The high oxygen content of reformulated gasoline will serve to increase NOx emissions, one of the two precursors necessary for photochemical ozone reaction.[2] Also, as aromatics are heavy HCs with a low propensity to evaporate, the reduction of aromatics content may not significantly affect the airborne concentration of reactive HCs, the other component of the photochemical ozone reaction. According to the initial findings of a research programme being conducted by major oil companies and auto manufacturers 'reducing aromatics...can either reduce or increase exhaust emissions, depending upon vehicle type.'[3] The impact of aromatics restrictions on ozone formation will also depend on whether ambient air concentrations of light hydrocarbons, derived from evaporative and running losses, or heavy hydrocarbons, emitted from the exhaust, are the major contributors to this environmental hazard.[4]

The root of the problem is that experts understand ozone formation only in the vaguest terms and, so, are unable to model effectively the impact of NOx or HC emission reduction on ozone levels. Other factors beside transport, such as hydrocarbon emissions from trees in US cities and, most especially, the weather, add many dimensions to the problem. The danger is that legislature will continue to tinker in various ways with the environmental issue, as it has done for the past twenty years, without having any impact on the ozone problem.

Other requirements imposed on vehicle manufacturers by the 1990 CAAA will make CO emissions from the tailpipe increasingly insensitive to the high oxygen content of new gasolines. From 1994 all new vehicles will be fitted with emission control diagnostic systems[5] and will be tested for CO emissions during 'cold start',[6] that is: starting the engine at 20

---

2   Another complexity of the impact of oxygenates on vehicle emissions is that their lower energy content, relative to ordinary gasoline, means that oxygenates may reduce the weight of emissions in comparison with ordinary gasolines on a volume basis but not on a BTU basis.

3   Auto/Oil Air Quality Improvement Research Program News Release, 18 December 1990 cited by G. H. Unzelman, 'U.S. Clean Air Act expands role for oxygenates', *Oil and Gas Journal*, 15 April 1991 p.45.

4   G. H. Unzelman, 'Oxygenate/hydrocarbon shift will rewrite gasoline recipes', *Oil and Gas Journal*, 29 April 1991.

degrees Fahrenheit. The emissions control diagnostic system will include an oxygen sensor able to monitor CO emissions and change engine temperatures to minimize those emissions. This system will reduce the impact of fuel properties on emissions while the engine is running. The cold start standards, on the other hand, will reduce the impact of fuel properties on CO emissions when the engine is turned on.

Tackling the problem of ozone and CO will be made more difficult by Congress's decision to mandate the fuels for specific geographic areas. This geospecific approach will not prevent vehicles with ordinary gasoline from entering nonattainment areas or, indeed, vehicles with new gasoline leaving the area. Furthermore, drivers on the outskirts of nonattainment areas may well be encouraged to purchase gasoline from a neighbouring attainment area if there is a price incentive to do so.

The third environmental objective associated with reformulated gasoline is the reduction in toxic emissions through restrictions on overall aromatics content and, more especially, on benzene content. The problems involved in estimating the possible benefits of such restrictions are that firstly there are long time lags involved with cancer manifestations that make it almost impossible to link causes and effects and, second, that it would require vast resources to collect enough information on the toxicity of other hydrocarbon compounds that may replace benzene in order to evaluate whether such restrictions reduced the overall toxicity of gasoline.

The new fuel regulations are a result of US public concern over urban pollution. If, however, the spectre of global warming materializes during the next decade then the US public may well begin to view the 1990 CAAA fuel regulations as ill-conceived. The production of new automotive fuels will increase refinery emissions of carbon dioxide considerably because of

---

5   See glossary for definition and The Clean Air Act Amendments, 1990, Title II, Section 207.

6   The Clean Air Act Amendments, 1990, Title II, Section 204.

the added need for processing gasoline- and diesel-blending components. If, in addition to this, the supply of new fuels is not seen to be cleaning the air of ozone and carbon monoxide then it is not unlikely that, as with the phasing out of lead, the legislation will be repealed or, even, reversed.

For refiners preparing to invest unprecedented sums in order to meet the terms of the 1990 CAAA these uncertainties can only mean one thing: the pay-back period for any investment must be shortened in the company's final analysis.

The huge investment required in oxygenate capacity seems risky as their environmental benefit in the long term is negligible; despite this, many refiners justify the investment as any other in a good octane-enhancing gasoline-blending component. However, making such an investment at a time when demand prospects are flat seems to go against the grain.

3.3   The Ambiguities of CAAA Provisions on Motor Fuels

Title II of the 1990 CAAA, which regulates pollution from mobile sources, will be the most politically controversial of the new provisions. Whereas the rest of the amendments apply only to industry, Title II will affect everyday lives. For this reason and because of the complexities involved in regulating mobile, as opposed to stationary, pollution sources the legislation is tentative and, so, open to a variety of interpretations.

Although the first specification for reformulated gasoline has been approved by the EPA (see Chapter 2) fuel suppliers may present their own specifications for 'certification'.[7] These proposals will be certified by the EPA as reformulated gasoline if they 'achieve equivalent or greater reductions in emissions of ozone forming volatile organic compounds and emissions of toxic air pollutants'.[8]

In addition the 'Reg-Neg' agreement of August 1991 has

---

7   The Clean Air Act Amendments, 1990, Title II, Section 219.

8   Ibid. See also glossary for definition of toxic air pollutant.

established that phase one reformulated gasolines must be 'recertified' in 1997 through the use of a more complex model than that which will be used in preparation for 1995 production start-up. This provision admits the possibility that refiners may have to comply with progressively more stringent specifications.

Certification may make feasible a totally new technical solution for the reformulation of gasoline.[9] This would create opportunities for refiners to undercut the costs of others. However, it will also have a retarding affect on the pace of the investment due to the incentive created for R&D. The appearance of a 'slate' of reformulated fuels in 1995 may also place unacceptable stress on the distribution system and, so, delay implementation.

A longer-term concern of fuel suppliers is the 1990 CAAA mandate for phase two reformulated gasoline. Phase two is aimed at reducing gasoline vehicle emissions by a further 20 to 25 per cent. This 20 to 25 per cent represents a huge increase over phase one requirements not only in absolute but also in relative terms, since as vehicle emission standards become more stringent vehicle emissions become less sensitive to fuel properties. As yet there is no indication as to which fuel properties could achieve such a reduction.

Phase two reformulated gasoline has dire implications for refiners' expenditures and profit margins. The emission requirement for phase two reformulated gasoline is very large and the date allocated for production start-up, ie. 2000, is very near. This means that refiners may only have at most five years in which to recoup their investments in phase one reformulated gasoline during which time they will have to invest in producing phase two specifications. Considering the cost involved in phase one production it is unlikely that the EPA will be able to enforce phase two according to the spirit in which the legislation was intended.

---

9   Other possible technical solutions include reduction of olefin content, desulphurization or increasing the boiling range of the gasoline cut from the distillation column.

Projections of future demand for new motor car fuels are crucial to refiners' perception both of costs and their ability to recoup those costs. The outcome of two provisions within Title II, namely the 'opt-in' and waiver clauses, will be the main determinants of future demand. Other ozone nonattainment areas will be able to opt-in in the case of both clean fuel and reformulated gasoline programmes. For clean fuels the impact on demand will be gradual as states will only be allowed to introduce economic incentives in order to encourage 'voluntary' opting in. However, reformulated gasoline can be mandated with as little as one year's notice to fuel suppliers. Therefore, if the opt-in clause is fully subscribed to, the demand for reformulated gasoline could more than double, from 22 to 55 per cent of US gasoline supplies,[10] within one year.

Whilst refiners prepare for the possibility of increased demand and, therefore, sharply increased costs; they also face the prospect that demand may fall if EPA's right to waive phase one oxygenated and reformulated gasoline deadlines is exercised. The EPA's right may be exercised if 'for any area' there is 'inadequate supply of, or distribution capacity for' the gasolines.

The waiver clause has been made less concilliatory by the 'Reg-Neg' agreement of August 1991 between the EPA and the oil industry. This states that to employ the waiver the EPA must judge that 'the refiner exercised prudent planning and was not able to avoid the violation and has taken all reasonable steps to minimize the extent of the nonconformity' otherwise the refiner may be liable to 'pay the U.S. Treasury an amount equal to the economic benefit of the nonconformity'.

If deadlines are waived, up to two years in the case of oxygenated gasoline and three years in the case of reformulated gasoline, then new gasolines will have to compete with lower priced unleaded. Such direct competition will almost certainly delay the payback of refiners' investments. Some refiners may

---

10 Dr C. H. Tahmassebi claims that 80 per cent of US supplies would need to be reformulated if the opt-in provision was fully subscribed to. See *Oxford Energy Forum*, OIES August 1991, Issue No.6.

choose to hedge against this uncertainty by investing to coincide with the end of the waiver period. However, in so doing refiners risk losing traditional markets if waivers are not exercised.

These inherent uncertainties exert opposing pressures on the investment strategies of refiners. On the one hand, current specifications for reformulated gasoline have been designed to enable refiners to start production by 1 January 1995. On the other, the 'certification' provision creates an incentive for refiners to delay investment while their R&D teams investigate alternative technical solutions to emission reductions. The effect of waivers and opting in is to make demand projections for reformulated motor car fuels almost wholly unpredictable, and consequently refiners will be looking closely at each other's investment decisions.

3.4   The Effects of Other Provisions of the 1990 CAAA on Green Fuel Supplies

Environmental regulations that do not directly concern product reformulations may still affect refiners' ability to meet the requirements of new motor fuels. The oil industry is particularly concerned over the possible implications of Title III of the 1990 CAAA, relating to hazardous air pollutants (HAP), and Title V, relating to permits (see Annex 2).

Title III of the 1990 CAAA may involve disincentives for the investments called for in the legislation and/or have an adverse effect on supply costs. Plants handling any one of the 189 listed HAPs will require Maximum Available Control Technology (MACT) to reduce emissions by 75 per cent by the year 2000. The sorts of pollution-control technologies required for listed HAPs will be mandated by the EPA in stages to 2000. The construction of any plant for the production, or use of listed HAPs, which is undertaken before MACT standards are promulgated, may require costly changes either during the construction period or soon after completion.

'Fuel suppliers' are in a particularly uncertain position because three substances crucial to the reformulation of motor car fuels, namely hydrofluoric (HF) acid, methanol and MTBE, were listed as HAPs in the 1990 CAAA. Yet the HF alkylation process[11] which, compared with its sulphuric acid-fed rival, produces twice as much gasoline and MTBE, is perceived by refiners as essential to meet both the aromatics and oxygen specifications of reformulated gasoline.

The effect of Title III on refiners will be to delay investment in increasing supplies of any listed HAPs as any construction undertaken before the EPA defines MACT requirements may have to incorporate costly changes. However, if supplies of those HAPs are not increased rapidly then the deadlines for green fuel programmes set by the 1990 CAAA may not be met.

The concern of oil companies over the HAP regulations is evidenced by the decision of many large refiners, namely Amoco, Ashland, Exxon, Phillips and Shell, to join a voluntary programme aiming to reduce toxic emissions of seventeen chemicals by 50 per cent by 1995.[12] Part of the estimated $4.8 to $6 billion cost of the programme[13] is attributed to the reduction in aromatics which refiners will phase in by 1995. Three of the seventeen targeted chemicals will be the aromatics compounds, benzene, toluene and xylene. Aromatics, and especially

---

11 The HF alkylation process produces around half the alkylate blended into US gasoline supplies; see 'Mobil boosts efforts to avoid ban on acid needed for reformulated gasoline', *Platt's Oilgram*, 5 March 1991, p.4.

12 'Majors join voluntary emissions cuts project', *Oil and Gas Journal*, 27 May 1991.

13 Shell claim their capital outlays will come to $400–500 million by 1995. As Shell produce approximately one-twelfth of total US refinery liquids we have interpolated the capital costs of the programme as a whole to be $4.8 to $6 billion. See 'Majors join voluntary emissions cuts project', ibid. Also 'recent estimates of capital investments for compliance with the CAA air toxics regulations for the entire US oil industry indicate that roughly $6 billion of capital investments may be required between 1992 and 1995.' See Dr C. H. Tahmassebi, 'Challenges facing refiners: environmental regulation in the USA', *Oxford Energy Forum*, OIES August 1991, Issue No.6.

benzene, restrictions may mean that refiners will extract these compounds from the CRU yield (see Chapter 3) thereby increasing the costs of handling these targeted chemicals.

The revised scheme for permits outlined in Title V of the 1990 CAAA may both increase the cost of producing new motor fuels and delay investments. Refiners in nonattainment areas will be forced to offset any emissions increase by compensatory reduction from another facility in the same area. The compensatory reduction must exceed the proposed increase by between 10 and 100 per cent depending on the area. Refining will be particularly hard hit as between 70 and 90 per cent of refineries are located in ozone nonattainment areas.[14] Permits will be required not only for construction but also for any modifications made to the operating conditions of processes.

The provisions relating to HAPs and permits will increase the cost of providing new motor car fuels and will delay refiners' investment plans. Also, if the conditions are right, refiners may redirect investment from nonattainment to attainment areas.

3.5   The Administration of Green Fuel Regulations

The final form that the new motor car fuel regulations will take depends on the way they are administered by the EPA in conjunction with individual states and the oil industry. It is important, therefore, to analyse the vested interests of the four parties, namely Congress, the EPA, each state and the oil industry, and the avenues of influence each has on the implementation of the CAA motor fuel regulations. The impact of the motor fuel regulations on the US refining industry will, to a large extent, depend on this contest of political wills.

(a) Congress. Having created the 1990 CAAA, Congress must be

---

14   70 per cent figure from Scherr et al, 'Clean Air Act complicates refinery planning', *Oil and Gas Journal*, 27 May 1991 and 90 per cent figure from Michael Mason, a lobbyist with the American Petroleum Institute cited in 'API cites time factor in "gas" standards', *Platt's Oilgram*, 12 October 1990, p.1.

resigned to take the role of a back-seat driver. However, Congress may intervene if it feels that the Administrator has misinterpreted or failed to implement the legislation. The successive failures of government to bring US air quality to attainment standards by the applicable deadline has almost institutionalized the war of words between Congress and those involved in the implementation of the CAA. Traditionally, Congress has accused the EPA and its coadministrators of lacking political will, whereas the EPA accused Congress of producing misguided legislation and of setting unrealistic deadlines. Recently, Waxman of the House of Representatives declared that the detailed version of the permit programme produced by the EPA incorporated changes that were 'flagrantly illegal'.[15]

The degree to which Congress will be willing to press litigation against illegal interpretation of the 1990 CAAA by the EPA is yet to be seen. Litigation may only have the effect of delaying the environmental benefits of new fuel programmes.

(b) The Administration. The Bush Government, through the EPA and other administrative organs, will tend to moderate the impact of the 1990 CAAA. The government's vested interest lies first and foremost in the success of the US economy and, therefore, it is very concerned to minimize the high projected cost of the regulations.

The EPA will have considerable influence over the costs of the three titles of the 1990 CAAA crucial to the impact of motor fuel regulations, namely the provisions relating to mobile sources, HAPs and permits. With regard to the motor fuel regulations themselves the cost of compliance could be reduced through the 'waiver' and 'certification' clauses (see above). Also, although there is no provision for a waiver in the case of low-sulphur diesel it is reported[16] that the EPA will allow a two-year extension for smaller refiners.

The detailed workings of the certification clause, which must

---

15   Rep. Waxman cited in *Platt's Oilgram*, 2 May 1991, p.5.

be determined by the EPA, afford many opportunities for more or less severe interpretation of the 1990 CAAA's terms. The EPA must decide what baseline gasoline and vehicle type should be used in order to provide a framework from which to estimate the emission reduction properties of reformulated gasoline. Further the EPA must elaborate whether refiners are to use actual testing methods or a model, or even a combination, in order to demonstrate that a certain fuel formulation meets emission requirements. These and many more details provide the Administrator with much leaway in interpreting the 1990 CAAA.

The EPA also has the power to reduce the cost of compliance with HAP regulations for smaller operators in industry. The MACT provisions for HAPs require that each of the source categories and sub-categories reaches 'the average emission limitation achieved by the best performing 12 percent of the existing sources (for which the Administrator has emissions information).'[17] However, the collection of emissions data to identify sources and the division of category, and, more especially, sub-category sources has been left to the EPA to complete by October 1991. In practice this means that smaller facilities, placed in sub-categories, could be required to install less expensive pollution-control technologies than the larger facilities.[18]

The EPA is already attempting to moderate the impact of the permit programme. Rep. Waxman claimed that one of the EPA's amendments of the permit programme, namely allowing any pollution source in receipt of a permit to increase emissions

---

16 'There will be some relief for refinery systems of less than 137,500 b/d or individual refineries of less than 50,000 b/d, since the EPA is prepared to allow such refiners a two-year extension to comply with the new regulations.' Dr P. McDonald, 'Low-sulphur diesel: the refining industry's next headache?', *Oil Daily Energy Compass*, 27 February 1991.

17 The Clean Air Act Amendments, 1990, Title III, Section 301 (d)(3)(A).

18 F. Flam, 'The Clean Air Act: on stage again', *Chemicalweek*, 31 October 1990, p.9:

at will, was illegal (see above) and that this amendment would destroy the purpose of the programme. In response, William Rosenburg of the EPA claimed that if plants were not able to modify the operations of existing units without having to face up to 18 months delay in order to ratify an alteration in emissions from that unit, then facilities would not be able to meet the deadlines set by Congress itself. Both statements are true, and this suggests a great deal about the feasibility of achieving the desired emissions reductions within the time schedule set by Congress.

(c) The States. Within the 1990 CAAA's motor fuel regulations some scope is given to individual states to opt-in in the case of fuel programmes and to require greater HAP emission reductions than specified by Congress or the EPA. State legislation will affect both the extent of demand for reformulated gasoline and the cost of supplies. On the demand side there may be a lot of pressure on state legislatures to opt-in in the case of new gasoline programmes. However, the EPA may overrule that right through the use of waiver. On the supply side construction may be delayed and made more costly by stringent state legislation over pollution control technologies and emission offset requirements, especially with regard to hazardous air pollutants.

States have other avenues of influence on the refining industry through their own legislatures. The predisposition of state legislatures to leapfrog federal mandates is well evidenced. California has consistently proved to be the impetus behind Congressional legislation. The summer gasoline volatility restrictions had already been imposed on a state-by-state basis before they were sanctioned by Congress. This may precipitate, as it has done for HF alkylation in California[19], onerous safety regulations, investment in pollution control facilities and construction permit delays which could prove a serious deterrent to investment or even the continuation of

---

19 'Hydrogen fluoride use banned at 4 Calif. refineries', *Platt's Oilgram*, 9 April 1991, p.4.

process operations. A Louisiana bill has proposed a ban on the construction of, among others, refineries or chemical plants within five miles of any community.[20] State interference in the regulation of HAPs could only have an inflationary effect on refiners' costs or even restrict their ability to meet the new regulations by banning the construction of new plants.

(d) The Oil Industry. Without the compliance of industry both the states and the EPA will find implementation of the 1990 CAAA motor fuel regulations to be intensely bureaucratic and legalistic. This will have the effect of delaying implementation and, if the EPA decides to force compliance, of damaging US industry.

As in the 1980s, the dissent of the US refining industry is being voiced through their astronomical cost projections and predictions of large-scale 'rationalization'.

However, there is another side to the industry's public stance which was not so apparent in the 1980s. The industry has been keen to show its concern for the environment by preempting legislation. Reformulated gasolines are already on sale and, as mentioned before, some of the major oil companies, namely Amoco, Ashland, Exxon, Phillips and Shell, have joined a voluntary programme hoping to cut emissions of seventeen EPA-listed HAPs by 50 per cent by 1995.[21] As O'Keefe plainly advises: 'Look good by doing good'.[22]

This preemptive strategy is indicative of the mixture of coercion and opportunity the industry sees in the legislation. Joining such a voluntary programme can be used as a bargaining chip with which the company may gain credit in the form of a time extension to fulfil MACT requirements set by the EPA and, by so doing, reduce its costs relative to those faced by

20 'State solons accent environmental issues', *Oil and Gas Journal*, 2 July 1990, p.32.
21 'Majors join voluntary emissions cuts projects', *Oil and Gas Journal*, 27 May 1991, pp.111–2.
22 W. F. OKeefe, 'API's O'Keefe: environment still top issue for U.S. industry', *Oil and Gas Journal*, 6 May 1991.

other companies. For 'those companies that understand the strategic implications, the Clean Air Act Amendments also present new opportunities to create competitive advantages'.[23]

23   Scherr et al, op.cit.

4 THE COSTS OF GREENING MOTOR FUELS

4.1 Introduction

The subjects of this chapter are the technological requirements and the cost of supplying new motor car fuels. The phasing out of lead is considered first in order to provide a context for the current task of changing the composition of gasoline and how this has, in the past, affected the profitability of refiners' product yields. This background also affords an insight into refiners' outlook and, therefore, their preparedness to invest in the light of past experience.

Second, the subjects of technology and cost are analysed with relation to phase one automotive fuels detailed in the 1990 CAAA. Phase two reformulated and oxygenated gasolines will be required in 2000 and, so, represent a further cost to refiners during the late 1990s. An analysis of the costs of phase two production is premature as there is not enough information on which to base an informed guess.

4.2 Unleaded Gasoline and the Octane Push

The phasing out of lead in the 1980s forced refiners to find other ways to maintain the quality of gasoline. Unlike sulphur in diesel, lead is an additive used to improve the engine performance or octane quality of gasoline. The attraction of lead as an octane enhancer is that it is cheap and does not affect the volatility of gasoline. During the 1980s refiners replaced lead by increasing the concentration of high-octane hydrocarbons, such as aromatics and olefins, and by adding high-octane nonhydrocarbons, such as methyl-tertiary-butylether (MTBE).[1]

Upgrading the octane quality of gasoline-blending components increased capital and operating costs of refineries and reduced supplies. The primary octane-enhancing process used for upgrading was the naphtha-fed Catalytic Reforming Unit (CRU). The CRU is used to increase the high-octane aromatic concentration of naphtha for unleaded gasoline blending. In order to further raise octane, refiners increased the severity of CR operating conditions,[2] thereby increasing aromatic content of naphtha. However, these operational adjustments result in higher energy consumption and diminished yield from the CRU.

Changing the composition of US gasoline in order to raise hydrocarbon octane also resulted in increased gasoline volatility. The availability of high octane but volatile butane increased due to refinery process changes and, with the downward pressure on gasoline octane levels resulting from phasing out lead, butane became a valued gasoline-blending component. The Reid Vapour Pressure (RVP) of summertime gasoline has climbed from 9 RVP in 1971 to between 10 and 10.5 RVP in 1987 due primarily to increased butane blending.[3] A 9 RVP maximum for summer gasoline came into force in 1989.

Increasing production of other refinery gases due to process changes opened other opportunities for refiners to maximize gasoline octane. During the 1980s the shift in demand towards

---

1   Between 1980 and 1988 the aromatics content of US gasoline increased from 22 to 32.1 (vol.) per cent and the ether content increased from 0 to 1.4 (vol.) per cent. See G. H. Unzelman, 'Reformulated Fuels, Part 1', *Oil and Gas Journal*, 9 April 1990, p.44.

2   Process variables for the CRU include catalyst type and activity, reactor temperature and pressure, feed rate and catalyst volume and the ratio of hydrogen to hydrocarbon feed. For more information see R.A.Meyers (ed.), *Handbook of Petroleum Refining Processes*, McGraw-Hill Inc. 1986, Part 3.

3   See Atkinson, Cristofaro and Kolb 'Role of the Automobile in Urban Air Pollution' in Tester, Wood and Ferrari (eds), *Energy and the Environment in the 21st Century*, MIT 1991, p.187.

the lighter part of the barrel and the shift in supply towards heavier crude feedstock meant that refiners had to increase their cracking capacity. Investment in Fluid Catalytic Cracking Unit (FCCU) capacity increased the availability of a valuable by-product, namely isobutylene. Isobutylene may be used as a feedstock either for alkylation or for 'captive' etherification plants producing MTBE or ethyl-tertiary-butylether (ETBE). All three, namely alkylation and the two etherification processes, yield high octane and low RVP gasoline-blending components, thereby easing the octane and volatility pressures placed on refiners by product specifications.

Two of the product yields of gas processing, natural gasoline and butane, were phased out of US gasoline supplies in order to meet the respective challenges of phasing out lead and volatility restrictions on gasoline.[4] These environmental regulations, therefore, took all the value-added refiners obtained from these two yields and relegated them, for refiners without petrochemical interests, to the status of petrochemical feedstock or refinery fuel. A refiner operating a complex[5] plant, integrated petrochemical facilities or with an interest in petrochemical plants has other options: he may use the butane rejected from finished gasoline to produce alkylate, ether or butadiene, a primary petrochemical material.

The legacy of the 1980s for US refiners is reduced competition and increased political uncertainty. The slump in demand in the early 1980s coupled with the need for investment created by shifts in the relative demand for products and environmental regulation, squeezed many of the smaller refiners out of the market. On the other hand political uncertainties have increased over the 1980s and affect refiners on two levels. The first uncertainty relates to the price at the pump. Supply shortages causing price spikes during winter

---

4   R. E. Canon, 'Environment and marketplace forcing major changes in gas processing', *Oil and Gas Journal*, 9 July 1990, pp.47–9.

5   See glossary under 'refinery complexity'.

1989 and the Gulf War attracted political criticism and in the latter case resulted in suppressed prices at the pump.

The second uncertainty relates to environmental issues. Environmental regulation has been shown to be short lived and reversible. As a result of the 1990 CAAA's restrictions on the aromatics and benzene content of new gasolines refiners will be forced to replace or further process the yield from the CRU. Refiners' returns from their initial investments in CRU capacity have been short lived and, now, the technological requirements of new gasolines have nullified the benefits of that investment. In the following two sections we consider the new technological requirements, their cost, the impact this will have on the composition of gasoline and diesel and the implications of this change in composition for the profitability of refiners' yields.

4.3   The Technical Solution to the Supply of Green Fuels

4.3.1 Assumptions

By 1995 fuel suppliers will be forced to reformulate gasoline and diesel supplies and to produce up to three new types of automotive fuel: reformulated gasoline, oxygenated gasoline and 'clean' fuel. However, as is obvious from the current legislation (see section 2.3) the future is made more opaque by Congress's reluctance to give clear mandates regarding the content, production start-up and future supplies of new fuels in the 1990 CAAA. Also, in order to estimate the impact of refiners' costs on the wholesale price of gasoline we shall make assumptions as to the recovery of that cost. Without such assumptions there is insufficient information from which to make such an analysis. The assumptions, and the reasons behind them, are as follows:

(a) Supplies. For the purpose of our analysis we have assumed that US demand for gasoline and diesel will remain flat during the 1990s and that the geographical distribution of that

demand will also stay the same. Firstly, we assume that refiners will choose to reformulate automotive diesel supplies, 1.38 mb/d in 1989, rather than the whole of the distillate pool. Second, we assume that, if the opt-in clause is not waived, around 50 per cent of US gasoline supplies, which average 7.3 mb/d, will need to be reformulated. Third, we assume that the oxygenate fuel programme, again if it is not waived, will require the oxygenation of 30 per cent of US winter gasoline supplies, which average 7.2 mb/d, from 1 November to 1 March of each year.

The assumptions made for future volumes of 'green' diesel fuel are straightforward whereas those for 'green' gasolines are not so. First, the 1990 CAAA mandates the reformulation of all diesel supplies but only mandates the supply of green gasolines for certain areas within the USA. Projections of gasoline sales in these areas are uncertain because of various factors associated with the distributional infrastructure and open-ended provisions contained in the 1990 CAAA.

On the physical side, perhaps price differences between gasolines at the same petrol station or in neighbouring areas will suppress demand for the more expensive gasoline brands. Conversely, distributional constraints may force the supply of new gasolines to replace conventional gasolines in both neighbouring attainment and nonattainment areas, thereby increasing required volumes over the short term. Further, the current supply of 'green' gasoline to attainment areas may not be allowed to be diverted to nonattainment areas. This would force refiners to produce additional quantities of oxygenate.

On the political side, ozone nonattainment states will be allowed to opt-in in the case of the reformulated gasoline programme. It is likely that most states will be tempted to opt-in as the reformulated fuel programme will aid them to meet the ozone attainment deadlines set in the 1990 CAAA. The upper limit on the required volume of reformulated gasoline if the opt-in clause is fully subscribed to varies between 50 and 80 per cent of US gasoline supplies. We have assumed that the opt-in clause will cause the required volume to range between 22 and 55 per cent of US gasoline supplies and that the opt-in offer will almost be fully subscribed to.

However, the supply of 'green' gasolines may be waived for any of these areas if the EPA deems that the supply of new gasolines is insufficient. Projections of gasoline sales in mandated areas may, in the case of reformulated gasoline sales in 1995, range from 0 to 25 per cent of total gasoline sales on the lowest side to between 55 and 80 per cent on the highest side.

(b) Content. Of the fuels under consideration in our analysis only the contents of reformulated gasoline and clean fuel have been left unspecified. The specifications for new diesel are 0.05 per cent sulphur maximum by weight and a minimum of 40 on the cetane index. The specification for oxygenated gasoline is simply a minimum oxygen content of 2.7 per cent by weight.

For reformulated gasoline we presume that the specifications currently proposed by Congress, namely 2 per cent minimum oxygen content by weight, 1 per cent benzene maximum by volume and 25 per cent aromatics maximum by volume will be adopted. However, these specifications err on the conservative side as it seems that additional restrictions will need to be imposed on reformulated gasoline in order for the fuel to achieve the motor car emission reductions required of it in the 1990 CAAA, namely 15 per cent for both toxics over the year as a whole and VOCs over the summer months.

However, between October 1990, when the amendments were passed by Congress, and October 1991, when the first of the phase one reformulated gasoline specifications will be ratified by the EPA, only the specifications proposed by Congress will provide a sure basis for investment.[6] US refiners

---

6   The major refiners and automakers are taking part in an R&D progamme to assess the impact of fuel compositions on vehicle emissions. The results of this task force will help those involved to second guess any future fuel formulations that the EPA may 'certify' as reformulated gasoline. However, it is unlikely that any refiner would start an investment programme based on such results without first seeking EPA approval for a new formulation along alternative lines than that proposed by Congress.

are safe in the knowledge that among the reformulated gasoline formulae ratified by the EPA (see Chapter 3, the certification clause of the 1990 amendments) will be one formulation that corresponds to specifications the same as, or more stringent than those proposed by Congress in October 1990. In this way Congress have guaranteed that any investment made between October 1990 and October 1991 on the basis of Congress's proposal will go some, or all of the way to meeting the requirements mandated for 1 January 1995.

We have discounted the production of clean fuels in our cost analysis as it will account for a minimal proportion of overall cost and that cost may be borne by chemical companies rather than refiners. However, we consider the impact of future demand for clean fuel in terms of the pressure this may exert on meeting minimum oxygen requirements for new gasolines. For this reason we assume that methanol or methanol-blends will be the clean fuel of choice.

(c) Production Start-Up. The supply of new diesel is mandated for 1 October 1993; however, the mandate for 'green' gasolines is complicated by the provision of a waiver. We assume that waivers, up to two years in the case of oxygenated gasoline and three years in the case of reformulated gasoline, will not be employed by the EPA and, so, supply will be mandated on 1 November 1992 for phase one oxygenated gasoline and 1 January 1995 for phase one reformulated gasoline.

(d) Capital Recovery. For each of the three fuels included in Table 5 we have assumed that refiners will recover their capital expenditures on the wholesale price of the same product on which the expenditures were made (in fact refiners will attempt to recoup their costs from any of their product yields) over a six-year period at a 15 per cent per annum rate of return.

The impact of the most likely technical solution for reformulating gasoline on the composition of future gasoline supplies is presented in Tables 3 and 4.

As petroleum refining is a simultaneous and highly integrated process the specifications for one product have ramifications for the supply of other products. This makes it difficult to structure any analysis as each part will automatically have linkages with every other. Bearing this in mind we shall consider four issues in turn: the oxygen requirements for oxygenated and reformulated gasoline, the aromatics (including benzene) restrictions on reformulated gasoline, the diesel fuel specifications and clean fuel requirements. For each we examine several possible technical solutions and whether these solutions may result in increased capital and/or operating costs.

4.3.2 Oxygenating gasoline

The minimum oxygen specification for reformulated and oxygenated gasolines will require the blending of liquids with high oxygen content and good gasoline qualities, known as 'oxygenates'. The oxygenates under consideration are non-hydrocarbon ethers or alcohols. Alcohols have been more or less ruled out because of their water solubility and the difficulties this causes in distribution. Ethers, such as MTBE, ETBE and tertiary-amylmethylether (TAME), seem set to be the refiners' choice. Phase one reformulated and oxygenated gasolines will have a minimum oxygen content of 2.0 and 2.7 per cent by weights which will require the blending of 11 and 15 per cent MTBE by volumes respectively.[7]

To obtain oxygenate supplies, refiners covered by the 1990 CAAA regulations will be forced either to invest in petrochemical production facilities or to buy on the spot market. If refiners choose to invest in their own oxygenate plants then they may elect either to invest in captive or grass roots facilities.

(a) Captive plants. Refiners with access to isobutylene supplies, either from a refinery FCCU or ethylene steam cracker,[8] are

---

7   G. Yepsen, T. Witoshkin, 'Refiners have options to deal with reformulated gasolnes', *Oil and Gas Journal*, 8 April 1991, p.69.

8   G. H. Unzelman, op.cit., p.46.

able to build small in-house MTBE or ETBE plants without large capital investments. Both MTBE and ETBE are synthesized using isobutylene, a light olefin yield of the FCCU, in conjunction with methanol and ethanol respectively. TAME production within refineries requires the supply of olefinic isoamylenes from the FCCU and methanol.[9]

The production of ethers within refineries will be restricted by the limited supply of light olefins, such as isobutylenes and isoamylenes, from refiner processes.[10] Light olefin production from the FCCU can be used as a feedstock for etherification and alkylation processes.[11] The capacity of all these processes and, therefore, light olefin supply will have to be increased if refiners are to meet reformulated gasoline specifications.

To increase light olefin supplies refiners will have to alter FCCU operations and catalysts.[12] By increasing the operating severity of the FCCU,[13] known as 'overcrack' mode, and by using selective catalysts refiners will be able to increase the availability of etherification and alkylation feedstocks. These changes in FCC operations will also help to reduce the benzene content of FCC gasoline thereby achieving another environmental objective set out in the 1990 CAAA. Also,

---

9   G. H. Unzelman, 'U.S. Clean Air Act expands role for oxygenates', *Oil and Gas Journal*, 15 April 1991, p.47.

10 Over the past three years the 22 MTBE plants located in refineries (ie. captive plants) were utilized at only 63.5 per cent of capacity (42,205 b/d in 1990). See 'Tenneco building Houston area MTBE plant', *Oil and Gas Journal*, 20 May 1991, pp.25–6.

11 MTBE and ETBE use isobutylene and TAME uses isoamylenes. Alkylation processes compete for both feedstocks.

12 R. H. Gilman, 'Capital outlays for gasoline reformulation can be minimized', *Oil and Gas Journal*, 3 September 1990, pp.44–9.

13 'Within the limits of normal operations, increasing 1. Reaction temperature, 2. Catalyst/oil ratio, 3. Catalyst activity, 4. Contact time results in an increase in conversion while a decrease in space velocity increases conversion.' J. H. Gary, G. E. Handwerk, *Petroleum Refining: Technology and Economics*, Marcel Dekker Inc. 1984, p.115.

increasing severity of the FCCU to overcrack mode will reduce gasoline yield and increase octane quality (see Tables 3 and 4).

(b) Grass-roots plants. However, purpose-built etherification plants require a large capital outlay to isomerize and dehydrogenate butane into isobutylene and, so, involve economies of scale.

By investing in purpose-built MTBE or ETBE plants refiners may use one environmental regulation, namely summer gasoline volatility restrictions, to satisfy another, namely minimum oxygen requirements of gasolines.[14] To meet summer volatility restrictions refiners will reduce the contribution of butane to finished gasolines. This butane could then be used as feedstock for MTBE or ETBE plants whose outputs will be needed to increase the oxygen content of new motor fuels. However, capital investment will be needed to increase storage capacity as there will be a seasonal mismatch between summer availability of butane feedstock and peak demand for oxygenates in the winter.[15]

(c) The Oxygenate spot market. The per barrel cost of producing oxygenates will depend on availability of feedstocks, the capacity of the construction service industry, tax credits, price of crude oil and technology used. The two main contenders for lowest cost oxygenate are MTBE and ETBE. ETBE scores over MTBE in terms of octane and lower volatility but costs around 30 per cent more per gallon to produce[16] because of the premium of ethanol over methanol feedstocks. However, ethanol and ETBE are eligible for federal and state tax credits that may make it competitive.

---

14 A. Seymour, 'US green gasoline: will it blur the distinction between refining and petrochemicals?', *Oxford Energy Forum*, OIES August 1990, Issue No.2.

15 Oxygenated gasoline will only be required for the winter months.

16 'US ethanol: a limited alternative to gasoline', *Petroleum Argus*, 29 October 1990, p.2.

4.3.3 Aromatics restrictions

The inclusion of oxygenate will dilute the aromatics concentration of finished gasoline, thereby helping to achieve the other specifications for reformulated gasoline, namely the 25 per cent aromatic and 1 per cent benzene maximums by volume.

The aromatic restrictions will reduce the total aromatic content of US motor car fuel supplies. The combination of a minimum cetane index for road diesel and a gasoline 'anti-dumping' clause[17] will prevent refiners from reblending rejected aromatics. However it is possible that aromatic-rich reformate will be exported.

The reduction in the aromatic content of finished gasoline will be achieved by reducing the contributions from two processes, namely the CRU and the FCCU. Most of the aromatics reduction will be achieved through the substitution of oxygenate for aromatic-rich reformate. Tables 3 and 4 have been derived with the assumption that some refiners will lower the operating severity of the CRU, reversing the trend begun by the phase out of lead and hydrotreat[18] the FCC feedstock[19] in order to further reduce the aromatic, and especially benzene, content of the CR and FCC gasoline yields. Hydrotreating the FCCU feedstock would also reduce the aromatic and sulphur content of road diesel. An option which many refiners are currently investing in is the isomerization of reformate in order to reduce benzene content.[20] This has the advantage of retaining higher utilization rates for the CRU, obviating the

---

17   This prevents refiners from reblending aromatics from finished gasoline in nonattainment areas to supplies in attainment areas. See The Clean Air Act Ammendments, 1990, Title II, Section 219(k)(8).

18   See glossary under 'desulphurization'.

19   Stokes et al, 'Reformulated gasoline will change FCC operations and catalysts', *Oil and Gas Journal*, 2 July 1990, pp.58–63.

20   G. Yepsen, T. Witoshkin, op.cit.

need for disinvestment.[21]

Aromatics restrictions may result in the redirection of straight-run[22] naphtha usually fed to the reformer. It is likely that the attractiveness of the alternative uses will depend greatly on the other interests of the refiner or parent company. Already many refiners are investing in additional isomerization capacity in order to retain naphtha as a gasoline-blending component and meet aromatics restrictions.[23] Refiners with petrochemical interests may continue to utilize reformer capacity and extract the aromatics for sale as an intermediate petrochemical product, however, the profitability of such a strategy will depend on future prices within that market.

Refiners are able to reduce CR operating severity without penalty to the quality of reformulated gasoline, in spite of the lower octane quality of low-severity reformate, because of the increased octane gained as a result of oxygenate blending.

The substitution of oxygenate for reformate will increase octane quality and RVP. Increased volatility of reformulated gasoline can cause problems for refiners in the summer months when there is a 9 RVP maximum specification for US gasolines. Also, refiners may have to reduce the volatility of summer gasoline further to 7.8 RVP in order to achieve the 15 per cent reduction in VOC emissions during the summer months.

The relaxation of octane pressures through investment in high octane ether production will allow refiners to reduce CR operational severity thus increasing reformate yield and reducing reformate RVP. However, refiners will have to further reduce RVP by backing out butane and replacing it with a low RVP alternative such as alkylate[24] (see Tables 3 and 4).

---

21 It is likely that refiners, if they choose to meet aromatics restrictions solely through a change in CRU operations, will have to reduce CRU utilization by a minimum of between 23 and 31 (vol.) per cent depending on operational severity of their CRU.

22 ie. derived directly from the distillation of crude oil.

23 L. R. Aalund, 'U.S. refining industry has powerful configuration', *Oil and Gas Journal*, 18 March 1991, pp.57–9.

Table 3: Estimated Composition of 1988 US Gasoline

	Volume Per Cent	Octane Range	Aromatics Range	RVP
Butane	7.0	91–93	–	52
Light Straight Run	3.3	55–75	0–4	11.1
Isomerate	5.0	80–88	–	13
FCC Gasoline	35.5	84–89	23–33	5
Hydrocrackate	2.0	85–87	2–6	4.6
Coker	0.6	60–70	4–8	13
Alkylate	11.2	90–94	–	7.9
Reformate	34.0	86–96	50–80	5.6
MTBE	1.4	106–110	–	9
Total	100.0			
Average Octane[25]		88.4		
Average Aromatics			32.2	
Average RVP				9.5

Sources: Compiled from G.H.Unzelman, *Oil and Gas Journal*, 9 April and 23 April, 1990; W.L. Leffler, op.cit., and R.H. Gilman, *Oil and Gas Journal*, 3 September 1990.

Another option to reduce RVP is for refiners to use ETBE instead of MTBE during the summer as it has similar octane quality and is half as volatile. The RVP specifications will increase the need for capital investment in additional etherification and alkylation capacity.

As mentioned before, Tables 3 and 4 detail the changes in gasoline-blending components which will be required to

24   Investment in C_4 isomerization could be used to convert butane into isobutane, a feedstock for alkylate.

25   The octane number is calculated by dividing the sum of the research octane and motor octane numbers by two ([RON + MON]/2). The average octane number is found by adding the mean of the octane ranges, each weighted by volume. The average octane number should be understood only in terms of a rough guideline as the blending octane numbers of some gasoline components may not be the same as [RON + MON]/2.

Table 4: Possible Composition of the Reformulated Gasoline Barrel

	Volume Per Cent	Change	Octane Range	Aromatics Range	RVP
Butane	2.0	−5.0	91–93	–	52
Light Straight Run	1.5	−1.5	55–75	0–4	11.1
Isomerate	8.0	+3.0	80–88	–	13
FCC Gasoline	35.0	−0.5	86–91	20–30	5
Hydrocrackate	2.5	+0.5	85–87	2–6	4.6
Alkylate	14.0	+3.0	90–94	–	7.9
Reformate	26.0	−8.0	82–92	45–75	5.3
MTBE	11.0	+9.6	106–110	–	9
Total	100.0	+0.6			
Average Octane			90.0		
Average Aromatics				24.5	
Average RVP					7.6

produce reformulated gasoline according to the specifications we have assumed. However, the need for capital investment is reduced by virtue of the fact that investment in these directions has been made since 1988.[26]

Taken on an aggregate level, therefore, the investment needed to produce reformulated and oxygenated gasoline will be in increasing oxygenate supplies, a variety of octane-enhancing capacities and on storage. To reduce the aromatics content of US gasoline refiners are likely to modify operations of the CRU and FCCU. Reducing the operational severity of the CRU will increase the yield of reformate but it will also reduce hydrogen production. We assume that the benefit in yield that refiners derive from reducing the operational severity of the CRU will be counterbalanced by the decrease in the value of that yield to refiners as a result of aromatics restrictions. However, the combination of a reduction in CRU hydrogen production and increase in refinery hydrogen consumption as a result of diesel fuel desulphurization (see below) may make large capital investment in hydrogen generation necessary. Also, to reformulate 50 per cent of US gasoline supplies refiners will need additional processing of gasoline blending components which will increase operating and production costs.

4.3.4   Diesel fuel specifications

Refiners have three main options to lower the sulphur content of 'on-highway' diesel supplies. The first is to buy lower-sulphur crudes. The second is to hydroprocess all distillate supplies so as to avoid the cost of segregating Numbers 1 and 2 automotive diesel from Number 4 ship diesel and Number 2 heating oil. The third option is to segregate diesel 1 and 2 for desulphurization and by so doing avoid the added expense of desulphurizing the other distillates.[27] If refiners elect for the first option in any great numbers then the price differential between sweet and sour crudes will increase until the cost of this option becomes prohibitive. The second option is also unfeasible as it will require huge capital investments in hydrogen generation and processing capacity.[28] Therefore, we have assumed that refiners will choose the third option.

Refiners will need to make operational changes and capital investments to produce reformulated diesel. A minimum cetane index of 40 for diesel will not require operational changes or investment as most US road diesel has a cetane index of between 45 and 47. However, the specification will serve to limit future refiner options that may result in reduced diesel quality, most especially using rejected aromatics from

27   L. Shyu, A. Bohn, op.cit.

28   R. A. Corbett, 'Tougher diesel specs could force major refining expenditures', *Oil and Gas Journal*, 30 March 1987, pp.56–9.

29   The cetane index, like the octane number for gasoline, is a measure of diesel quality. Although no exact relationship has been determined between the cetane index and aromatic content, in general cetane quality is inversely proportional to aromatics content.

gasoline for diesel blends.[29]

The desulphurization of diesel will require capital investment.[30] Many refiners will have to invest in additional hydroprocessing capacity, either hydrotreating the FCCU feedstock (see above) or post-treating road diesel. Others will be able to achieve the 0.05 per cent maximum sulphur content by weight by increasing operational severity and by using specialist hydrotreating catalysts.[31] Either way production costs for road diesel will increase due to lower throughput and increased hydrogen and energy consumption. Production costs and the need for investment will tend to increase over time as crude feedstocks become heavier or hydrogen-poorer and more sour or sulphur-richer.

As a result of road diesel desulphurization refiners may have to invest in additional storage and hydrogen production. Additional storage space, and possibly pipelines and terminals,[32] will be needed to separate road diesel from the rest of the middle distillate pool in order to preserve the lower sulphur characteristics of the former. Additional hydrogen production may be necessary as a result of increased demand for hydrodesulphurization and lower hydrogen supplies from the CRU.[33]

4.3.5 'Clean' fuel requirements

As of 1996 a number of service stations in California will be required to supply clean or alternative fuels. The clean fuel programme will spread to the nine worst nonattainment cities in 1998. It is probable that the choice of alternative fuel will be methanol or a methanol-blend. Like oxygenates, methanol is a

---

30   See R. A. Corbett, op.cit.

31   R. A. Corbett, 'New catalyst designs meet environmental challenges of the 1990s', *Oil and Gas Journal*, 1 October 1990, p.49.

32   Dr P. McDonald, 'Low-sulphur diesel: the refining industry's next headache?', *Oil Daily Energy Compass*, 27 February 1991.

33   Lower operating severity and possibly throughput of CRU will decrease hydrogen production of the unit.

petrochemical produced by chemical as well as oil companies. Refiners will be forced either to invest in non-hydrocarbon processes or relinquish their monopoly of automotive fuel supply to suppliers from outside the traditional industry. Whichever choice is taken by individual refiners the clean fuel programme will exert pressure on methanol supplies also in demand for the production of oxygenates, such as MTBE and TAME.

In conclusion, if the EPA adopts Congress's proposed specifications for reformulated gasoline then substantial investment and changes in operations will be required to produce new automotive fuels. Capital investment will be made in ether, alkylate, isomerate and hydrogen production, hydroprocessing capacity and storage. Refiners will also change the operating conditions of the CRU and FCCU. Costs may be reduced through optimizing blending systems[34] and catalyst specialization; however, operating and production costs will increase as a result of further processing.

The reformulation of automotive fuels will alter the qualities and quantities of the fuels. Gasolines will become less dense, less volatile and will have better octane quality. However, the energy content of ethers is lower than that of the oil-based reformate that they replaced. Therefore, the increasing octane quality of gasolines should increase the efficiency of motor cars and, so, increase miles per gallon whereas the lower energy content of green gasolines relative to conventional unleaded will serve to increase consumption per mile driven.

The available supply of gasoline blending components, most especially ether and reformate, will increase due to investment and operational changes. However, the outlook for on-highway diesel supplies is less certain. On the one hand, FCCU feedstock hydrotreating will increase conversion and, on the other, increased FCCU severity to maximize light ends will reduce the yield of light cycle oil, the primary road diesel blending component.

---

34   A. Hubel, Y. Serpemen, F. W. Wenzel, 'Modern fuel blending', *Oil and Gas Journal*, 18 March and 1 April 1991.

4.4   The Cost to Refiners

The refiner costs being considered here and presented in Table 5 are those directly related to the product specifications assumed above. The focus of this section is on oxygenated and reformulated gasolines and reformulated diesel. The cost of the other regulations, namely clean fuel and gasoline detergents, will either not be borne by refiners or will be negligible in comparison. The impact on these costs of uncertainties will be considered in the following chapter.

Table 5: The Cost of Green Fuels to Refiners and the Possible Effect on Wholesale Prices

Type of Fuel	Assumptions	Cost to Refiners		
		c/g	Capital Recovery ($mn/yr)	Operating ($mn/yr)
All Fuels	Capital recovery over six years subsequent to mandated production start-up with a return of 15 per cent per annum			
Phase I Oxygenated Gasoline	30 per cent of US winter gasoline supplies (7.2 mb/d on average) will have to be oxygenated (15 per cent volume of MTBE at a premium of 28 c/g over gasoline) for four months each year from November 1992	4.7		519
Reformulated Diesel	The regulations will require the reformulation of 1.38 mb/d road diesel by October 1993	4 to 6	423 to 635	423 to 635
Phase I Reformulated Gasoline	Reformulate 50 per cent of US gasoline supplies (7.3 mb/d on average) by 1995	8.2 to 11.0	2,014 to 3,021	2,574 to 3,133
Total			2,437 to 3,656	3,516 to 4,287

4.4.1   Oxygenated gasoline

Two crucial assumptions have been made to estimate the cost of oxygenates to refiners. The first assumption is that MTBE is the refiners' oxygenate of choice and the second is that the capital costs of constructing oxygenate plants will not be borne by refiners and that the premium of oxygenate over gasoline remains steady. The result of this approach is that the cost to refiners of oxygenating gasoline is expressed as an operating cost. This presents a conservative estimate of the cost of oxygenating gasoline as the prospect for increased oxygenate supply still does not match the projected minimum oxygen requirements of gasolines. Also, the rush to build grass-roots oxygenate plants coupled with other refinery and petrochemical capital investments is likely to put a premium on the construction industry servicing downstream oil interests. The capacity of this service industry has been halved since 1980. Inadequate oxygenate supply is likely to have an inflationary effect on the 'MTBE to gasoline' premium over the next few years unless, perhaps, EPA waivers of deadlines come into play.

On average MTBE is around 28 cents per US gallon (c/g) more expensive than the reformate it will replace.[35] Phase one reformulated gasoline will require around 11 per cent and phase one oxygenated gasoline 15 per cent MTBE by volume. This results in an additional cost of 3.1 c/g for oxygenating reformulated gasoline in 1995–9 and 4.2 c/g for oxygenated gasoline in the winters of 1992–9. The winter peak in oxygenate demand, due to coincidence of reformulated and oxygenated gasoline mandates during this season, will require additional storage for oxygenates. The US DOE have estimated that this will add 0.5 c/g on both the cost of reformulated and oxygenated gasolines.

Some argue that the higher octane quality of MTBE will enable refiners to lower reforming severity thereby reducing

---

35   'EPA: feasibility and cost of reformulated gasoline in the nine severe ozone areas', *New Fuels Report*, 14 May 1988, p.14.

processing costs and increasing yield. However, the rejection of reformate from US gasoline supplies will reduce the value of that yield to refiners. We assume that these factors balance out.

4.4.2   Reformulated gasoline

The most expensive green product will certainly be reformulated gasoline. On top of the cost of oxygenating reformulated gasoline, estimated at around 3.6 c/g (3.1 c/g for the oxygenate premium and 0.5 c/g for extra storage costs), refiners will also need to invest in reformulating the crude oil-derived portion of reformulated gasoline in order to meet aromatics restrictions.

Estimates of the costs of reformulating gasoline vary greatly. In part this is due to the sensitivity of cost estimates to assumptions, such as, the technical solutions to be adopted by refiners, the rate of capital recovery on capital investments and most especially the demand for reformulated gasoline. Currently oil companies, such as Sun, claim to be able to produce a type of reformulated gasoline for as little as a 2 to 5 c/g premium over regular unleaded because demand for it is limited and refiners can reblend the rejected aromatics into other gasoline types until 1995.[36] By 1995 cross-blending options will be limited by the anti-dumping clause of the 1990 CAAA (see previous chapter) and demand for reformulated gasoline will be far higher.

Another reason for the variance in cost estimates is that they are frequently used by interested groups as a means of political lobbying. Oil industry sources estimate that the cost of reformulating US gasoline supplies will increase the price at the pump by between 10 to 25 c/g on average. The extreme of this range was provided by the American Petroleum Institute (API) estimate of 20–5 c/g increase at the pump.[37] Strangely enough, the assumptions used in this estimate, namely 2.7 per cent minimum oxygen content by weight, 25 per cent aromatics

---

36   'Sun to unveil reformulated gasolines', *Platt's Oilgram*, 3 May 1991, p.3.

and 1 per cent benzene maximum by volume, and 25 per cent of US gasoline demand by 1995 are not extravagant. On the one hand, the estimate has included the extra cost of 4 per cent MTBE by volume (1 to 1.5 c/g) over that indicated by Congress and, on the other, the estimate uses the minimum demand scenario of 25 per cent. However, the estimate implies an increase of between 17 and 22 per cent in the average US city retail price of regular unleaded which was $1.16 per gallon in 1990.[38]

Dr Tahmassebi, the Chief Economist at Ashland Oil, supports Amoco's lower estimate of between 10 and 15 c/g, an increase of between 9 and 13 per cent in the retail price.[39] However, this lower range still implies a massive increase in refiner costs. If 80 per cent of US supplies are reformulated, which Dr Tahmassebi assumes as the upper limit if all the ozone nonattainment areas opt-in (see Chapter 2), this price rise translates to an increase in consumer spending of $9–13 billion per year at the current average US gasoline demand of 7.3 mb/d. Given the assumption[40] that refiners are not able to pass the full costs of compliance on to consumers at least over the short term and that many other costs will have to be borne as a result of other environmental regulations and for normal maintenance then this figure suggests even larger refiner expenditure. To place this in context: total US industry outlays

---

37   The American Petroleum Institute estimate for the same specifications and demand scenario was 20–5 c/g increase at the pump. See *Petroleum Intelligence Weekly*, 9 April 1990, p.8.

38   API, *Basic Petroleum Data*, May 1991, Section VI Table 12c.

39   Dr C. H. Tahmassebi, 'The environmental regulations and their impact on the U.S. refining industry', *Oxford Energy Forum*, OIES August 1991, Issue No.6.

40   Dr C. H. Tahmassebi, uses this same assumption in a previous paper entitled 'Recent Developments In Environmental Regulations And Their Impact On The U.S. Refining Industry', Proceedings of the Eleventh International Area Conference held at The International Research Center For Energy And Economic Development, University of Colorado, Boulder, CO, 29 April–1 May 1990.

on hydrocarbon processing were $7.5 billion for 1990, of this $4.4 billion was spent on refining and $3.1 billion on petrochemicals.[41]

From outside the oil industry John R. Dosher, vice-president of Pace Consultants Inc., estimates that refiner costs would increase by around 7 to 12 c/g.[42] In his estimate Dosher assumes specifications more stringent than those proposed by Congress but also uses the minimum demand scenario of 25 per cent. At the more probable demand scenario of 50 per cent reformulation of US gasoline supplies this cost estimate certainly seems plausible.

Our estimate for the increase in refiner costs to reformulate 50 per cent of US gasoline by 1995 is 8.2 to 11 c/g on average. This assumes that average US gasoline demand stays at 7.3 mb/d and that refiners will look for a 15 per cent return on capital expenditure over the six years subsequent to production start-up. Of that total 4.6 to 5.6 c/g is increased operating costs as a result of oxygenate blending (3.1 c/g) and storage (0.5 c/g) and increased processing of gasoline-blending components (1 to 2 c/g).

The remainder, namely 3.6 to 5.4 c/g, is for the capital recovery of $5.2 to $7.8 billion which I have estimated that refiners will need to invest by 1995.[43] This is based on a cost estimate by Gilman[44] of Akzo Chemicals. Gilman estimates that the average 100,000 b/d refinery would require capital

---

41   'Capital spending report', *Oil and Gas Journal*, 18 February 1991, p.21.

42   John R. Dosher cited in 'Pace: fuel requirements must be clearer', *Oil and Gas Journal*, 2 April 1990, p.20.

43   This estimate of capital expenditure is corroborated by Marathon Oil Company's plans to spend $135 million over the next three years to produce new gasolines out of $435 million set aside to comply with all provisions of the CAA (*Platt's Oilgram*, 6 February 1991, p.2). With 2.42 per cent of US liquids production this translates to industry-wide expenditures of $5.6 billion between 1992 and 1994 inclusive.

44   R. H. Gilman, op.cit.

investment of around \$58 million to produce 65,000 b/d reformulated gasoline.[45] Therefore to produce 7.3 mb/d of gasoline capital investment by refiners could reach around \$6.5 billion. To arrive at the final sum of \$5.2 to \$7.8 billion I have further included a 20 per cent margin of error in order to account for the inaccuracies of cost estimates based on outline engineering designs.[46] This upward margin of error is further justified by the expected increase in rates that the construction industry is expected to demand over the 1990s.

4.4.3   Low sulphur diesel

To desulphurize 1.38 mb/d of road diesel refiners will need additional hydroprocessing, hydrogen generating and storage capacity. Furthermore, their operating costs will increase as existing hydrotreating capacity is run at higher severity.

The cost estimates for diesel fuel desulphurization are similarly varied. The EPA estimates[47] that only a 1.8 to 2.3 c/g average increase in the retail price will be required to cover costs, whereas, the oil industry suggests that a 9.8 c/g increase in the average wholesale price would be required to compensate refiners.[48]

---

45 I have assumed that various factors in the estimate that conflict with my assumptions balance out. For instance that the cost of oxygenate production is balanced by the capital expenditure on hydrogen generation and hydroprocessing for saturation of aromatics and/or sulphur removal.

46 'In normal engineering practices for industrial projects cost estimates for outline designs are expected to have a 15 to 30 per cent margin of error.' A. Seymour, *The Oil Price and Non-OPEC Supplies*, OIES 1990, p.29.

47 L. Shyu, A. Bohn, op.cit.

48 This calculation uses oil industry estimates of \$2.8 billion in Capex and a \$1 billion increase in operating costs. In our calculation we assume demand for reformulated diesel stays around 1.38 mb/d and that refiners look for a 15 per cent return per annum over the six years subsequent to 1 October 1993.

The cost of implementing the legislation will be different for each refiner. Some will incur only increased operating costs but many more will have to make capital investments. BP Oil Co. has a planned 'environmental and efficiency expenditure' of some $500 million for two Ohio refineries over the next ten years and, of that, $100 million, or one-fifth, will be spent on a 127,000 b/sd hydrotreating unit for desulphurizing road diesel.[49]

In the light of these diverse views we have adopted a conservative estimate of 4 to 6 cents per gallon increase in the average wholesale price, divided equally between increased operating cost and capital recovered over a six year period. This estimate is based on the following assumptions: the US refining industry to desulphurize diesel fuel used on US highways will invest until 1 October 1993 between $1.1 and $1.6 billion and incur an increase in annual operating expenditure of $0.4 to $0.6 billion.

In conclusion: if the total costs for producing the three new types of motor car fuel are annualized for the period 1991 to 1999, inclusive, they would imply an increase in refiners' current expenditure of $2.8 to $3.6 billion.[50] This represents an increase of between 64 and 82 per cent over the total outlays (operating and capital) of $4.4 billion of the US refining industry in 1990. Our conservative estimate does not even include the cost of other environmental legislation.

It is interesting to note that over-all budgeted outlays for 1991 have increased by only 32 per cent from $4.4 billion in 1990 to $5.8 billion.[51] This may be indicative of the fact that

---

49 'BP outlines U.S. refinery spending plans', *Oil and Gas Journal*, 29 April 1991.

50 [Capital expenditures for reformulated gasoline (5.2 to 7.8) and diesel (1.1 to 1.6) + Operating expenditures for reformulated gasoline (12.9 to 15.7), reformulated diesel (2.5 to 3.8) and oxygenated gasoline (3.6)] divided by 9 to represent the years 1991 to 1999.

51 'Capital Spending Report', *Oil and Gas Journal*, 18 February 1991, p.21.

refiners are delaying investment until the significant uncertainties surrounding the motor car fuel regulations are more fully resolved.

This cost estimate should be considered as the lowest range of costs for reformulating motor fuels that refiners may face. As mentioned before, the costs of oxygenating gasoline are expressed as an operating cost or the current market price of substituting reformate by MTBE. This premium is likely to increase as the legislation comes into force.

In addition to this the estimate does not include the expenditures refiners will have to make in order to supply phase two reformulated gasoline in 2000 and, possibly, to 'recertify' phase one reformulated gasolines in 1997. Lack of information as to the probable composition of the Auto/Oil programme's complex model prevents us from making an informed estimate.

5   THE IMPACT ON REFINERY STRUCTURE, OIL COMPANIES' BEHAVIOUR AND THE MOTOR FUELS TRADE

5.1   The Impact of Green Fuel Supply on the US Refining Industry

Four factors stand out as being significant to the future structure and behaviour of the refining industry in the USA. The first is the high projected capital and operating expenditures for reformulating gasoline and diesel. The second is the increase in refinery imports of petrochemical feedstocks and products to satisfy the requirements of reformulated and oxygenated gasolines. The third is the reduction in value-added of many gasoline-blending components to refiners as a result of the rejection of these components from finished gasoline. The fourth is the segregation of consumer markets. Underlying all these developments are the uncertainties surrounding the legislation and the market.

The cost of meeting the 1990 CAAA's requirement is likely to dominate US refinery expenditures. The full cost of the 1990 CAAA to American refiners has been estimated at between $34 and $38 billion out of $70–100 billion required to bring refining and marketing in the USA into compliance with environmental regulations over the next decade.[1] From our estimate, current expenditure required to reformulate motor car fuels will range between $25 to $33 billion during the 1990s. However, these costs will vary from refinery to refinery depending on refinery

---

1   Scherr et al (ENSR consulting and Engineering, Houston), 'Clean air act complicates refinery planning', *Oil and Gas Journal*, 27 May 1991.

configuration and the environmental requirements particular to that location.

The cost of reformulating motor fuels will be large and the impact of these regulations on the US refining industry will depend on whether refiners are willing or able to raise the necessary sums.

Refiners, too small to generate the capital, will have to exit the market if they are not protected by government. A study by the General Accounting Office[2] claimed that 75 refiners with processing capacity of under 0.1 mb/d each, together comprising between 0.9 and 1 mb/d (some 13 per cent) of total US gasoline production, could be threatened. The two most vulnerable types of refinery will be small refineries, 50,000 b/d or under, which account for around 2.1 mb/d some 13 per cent of US distillation capacity, and old refineries; most especially refineries in these categories that are located in ozone nonattainment areas. Even the large companies have been quick to identify old refineries which could prove unprofitable to upgrade. Shell have already decided to close their 133,000 b/d Wilmington refinery in California and rumours are circulating over Sun's 125,000 b/d Toledo, Ohio plant. The fate of small refiners will very much depend on the degree of protection afforded to them by the Administration. Some 'subsidies' are being offered refiners of 100,000 b/d or less toward highway diesel sulphur restrictions. However, none has yet been offered with respect to reformulated gasoline. This glimmer of hope has not prevented Philips from looking for buyers for its 25,000 b/d Woods Cross, Utah plant.

Another possibility is that economies of scale involved in some of the investments, desulphurization and purpose-built oxygenate plants for instance, may encourage refiners to merge operations. However, American law governing mergers is very stringent indeed and attempts by different refiners to merge certain operations may be blocked.

---

2   General Accounting Office, 'Uncertainties surround reformulated gasoline as a motor fuel' cited in 'GAO: reformulation threatens small refiners', *Oil and Gas Journal*, 2 July 1990, p.34.

The ability to raise this order of capital is not at issue for those refiners with large parent companies. However, the large refiner's willingness to invest will depend more on their perception of the future profitability than on their parent company's ability to raise capital. One part of the profitability equation for refiners is the cost of supplying new motor fuels which, even if we discount the impact of significant uncertainties inherent in the 1990 CAAA (see Chapter 3), are far from predictable.

In the second instance, refineries will be increasingly dependent on petrochemical feedstocks or products to produce new gasolines. Except in the very rare cases where petrochemical production is fully integrated within the refinery,[3] refiners will need to import petrochemical feedstocks and/or products. Petrochemicals, such as ETBE or MTBE, will be needed to satisfy the oxygen requirements of new gasolines. If refiners decide to synthesize ETBE or MTBE within the refinery then they may need to import petrochemical feedstocks, such as ethanol and methanol. Also, both alkylation and etherification processes, whose capacities will need expanding in order to produce new gasolines, use isobutylenes and amylenes that can be derived from either refiner or petrochemical processes, namely: the FCCU or ethylene steam cracker, respectively. As the US refinery supply of isobutylene and amylene feedstocks is being fully utilized at present, refiners may have to import these feedstocks from petrochemical plants if they wish to increase the capacities of captive alkylation and etherification processes.

Further, traditional chemical products will become increasingly dependent on refiner markets. Until the 1980s methanol was used solely in the chemical industry for the production of formaldehyde and acetic acid. However, over the next decade methanol production is expected to double. 'The largest single use for methanol by the end of the next decade is

---

3   See the example of the German Gelsenkirchin refinery in A. Hubel, Y. Serpemen, F. W. Wenzel, 'Modern fuel blending – 1', *Oil and Gas Journal*, 18 March 1991, pp.62–74.

expected to be in liquid fuels. This application will include motor fuel, motor fuel additives, and fuel for power generation.'[4]

However, the traffic between petrochemical plants and refineries will not be one way. As a result of environmental regulations refinery products previously used in finished gasoline will now have to be further processed and/or find other markets. A good example of the symbiotic relationship between refineries and petrochemical plants generated as a result of environmental regulations is that of butane, rejected from summer gasoline supplies to reduce volatility, and MTBE, blended to meet oxygen requirements. The surplus summer butane from refineries will be needed as feedstock for purpose-built MTBE plants.

The aromatics restrictions for reformulated gasoline will affect refiners' demand for naphtha. Naphtha is rich in aromatic compounds. Aromatic compounds are intermediate products for both the refining and petrochemical industries. For petrochemical plants, aromatic compounds, principally benzene, toluene and xylene, are extracted from aromatic-rich products, such as naphtha, for the production of a wide variety of petrochemical products. In refining, aromatics are valuable gasoline-blending components because of their high octane and low RVP qualities; however, these qualities have now been rejected due to the environmental impacts of aromatic compounds. If refiners wish to retain the naphtha constituency of gasoline then they will have to use alternative octane-enhancing units, other than the CRU which maximizes aromatics content, to process naphtha. One option may be to hydrocrack naphtha.

In order to maintain gasoline qualities, namely volatility and octane, in the face of future environmental regulations refiners will have to process hydrocarbons formerly blended directly into finished gasoline. Butane will have to be

---

4   H. L. List, *Petrochemical Technology: An Overview For Decision makers in the International Petrochemical Industry*, Harvey L. List 1986, p.19.

isomerized in order to supply additional alkylation capacity. Hydrotreating the FCCU feedstock may be necessary to meet reformulated gasoline and diesel specifications. Reformate and straight-run gasoline will now be increasingly channelled through the isomerization unit, in the former case to increase octane quality[5] and in the latter to reduce benzene content.[6] The technological complexity of refineries will be relevant, therefore, to the ability of refiners to produce the new motor car fuels without suffering a reduction in the yield of motor car fuels.

The increasing geographical segregation of consumer markets is the fourth and most difficult factor to consider in terms of its impact on the structure and behaviour of American refining. It is important to bear in mind that only demand, not supply, will be segregated. Fuel suppliers have, therefore, the choice of whether to invest in producing the new fuels near consumer markets or further away. The cost of transportation will naturally incline refiners to invest in refineries near to consumer markets. However, those refineries near new markets will be located in nonattainment areas. The construction permit scheme is more stringent in nonattainment areas and therefore investment per unit output may be higher for refineries near consumer markets. Also, as only 30 per cent of refineries operate in attainment areas refiner choice may be limited. On the other hand, permit requirements may vary state-by-state creating other externalities. In considering the impact of the increasing segregation of consumer markets the refiner must balance between the additional environmental expenditure of investing near to the market and the cost of expanding the distributional infrastructure.

The opportunities for relocating refining capacity are limited by two factors. The first constraint is the difficulty of obtaining

5   R. H. Gilman, 'Capital outlays for gasoline reformulation can be minimized', *Oil and Gas Journal*, 3 September 1990.

6   G. Yepsen, T. Witoshkin, 'Refiners have options to deal with reformulated gasoline', *Oil and Gas Journal*, 8 April 1991.

planning permission to build a new facility in the USA. In some areas, such as the west coast, planning permission is considered to be unattainable. The second constraint is imposed on refinery construction by the large capital costs associated with adding significantly to the current pipeline network.

The two main centres of demand for new motor car fuels will be the west coast and the north-eastern states, both ozone and CO nonattainment areas. The gasoline market on the west coast is isolated from other markets as it is not linked by pipeline to any other sources of supply outside the west coast. More than half of the refining and pipeline capacity in California is owned by Atlantic Richfield, Chevron, Shell,[7] and Unocal. These companies guard their respective market shares jealously and are able to create many obstacles to entry either through price cutting[8] or pipeline tarriffs.[9] Competition in the supply of new gasolines to the west coast is more likely to come from the Far East, which is investing heavily in alkylation and isomerization gasoline-enhancing capacity,[10] than from other areas within the USA.

The north-eastern states receive their gasoline almost solely from the gulf coast and from imports. In 1988 the two sources supplied 1.45 mb/d and 0.36 mb/d respectively and together accounted for 97 per cent of imports to PADD I (this covers the whole east coast) with the remaining 3 per cent being supplied from PADD II (this covers the US Midcontinent and the

---

7   Shell's share of Californian refining capacity dropped from 12 to 7 per cent (see *Platt's Oilgram*) when it decided to put its 133,000 b/d Wilmington refinery up for sale on 25 June 1991.

8   Atlantic Richfield, Chevron and Shell became involved in a price war at Californian pumps 'in the 1st quarter as the majors fought for market share at a time when product demand was weak'; Philip Lambert of Kleinwort Benson Securities, *Ultramar*, April 1991, p.14.

9   See 'Calif. independents want "burden" of proprietary pipelines lifted', *Platt's Oilgram*, 27 February 1991.

10 A. Seymour, *The World Refining System and Oil Products Trade*, OIES 1990, pp.11–12.

Midwest). However, due to the difficulties foreign refiners may face in producing new gasolines additional supply may have to be found from PADD III (the gulf coast) or PADD II. One of the factors which refiners will be influenced by in their decision on whether to expand refining capacity in PADD II or PADD III will be the extra cost of meeting permit requirements in PADD III, an ozone nonattainment area, relative to PADD II, an ozone attainment area.

Many of the uncertainties surrounding the legislation governing new motor car fuels will be seen by refiners in terms of additional R&D opportunities. Advances in catalysts, blending systems and octane-enhancing processes will play a large part in minimizing capital expenditures. However, the biggest R&D opportunities are to be found in the uncertainties that surround the 1990 CAA. The prime example of this is the specifications for reformulated gasoline. Refiner options to achieve emission specifications include desulphurization[11] or reducing the olefininc content of gasoline. Companies are currently embarked on long auto emission research programmes in order to locate the secret formula that will achieve the emission reductions at lowest cost. This may lead to very different technical solutions being adopted by each refiner, thereby causing an increased range of possible cost curves.

As they appear today, the 1990 product reformulations will reinforce the structural trends of the 1980s. The qualities that may afford refining companies a competitive edge, by virtue of environmental regulation, in the automotive fuel markets of the future are vertical integration, technological complexity and R&D expenditure.

5.2   The International Trade in Motor Fuels

The green fuel regulations contained in the 1990 CAAA will have complex ramifications for oil markets in the USA and, so,

---

11 'GM mounts push for reformulated motor fuel now', *Oil and Gas Journal*, 25 March 1991, pp.28–9.

to foreign suppliers of those markets. As a result of the changing supply and demand relationship, the residual US oil and oil product requirements will also change – thereby altering the pattern of world motor fuels trade.

(a) Supplies. Available supplies of gasoline and on-highway diesel are expected to increase over the 1990s as a result of investment and changes in refinery operations. However, this outcome assumes that additional supplies will outweigh the negative effects of capacity rationalization and exit from motor fuel markets.

Diesel supplies are expected to be adequate when new diesel specifications come into force on 1 October 1993. Initial concerns that the exit of many small refiners from the highway diesel market due to the high costs of desulphurization may result in reduced supplies, have been counter-balanced by the preparedness of larger refiners to invest in desulphurizing all their distillate supplies.

The major additions to gasoline supply will result from the increased availabilities of reformate and MTBE. Many refiners will be able to reduce the operating severity of the CRU because of the additional octane afforded through oxygenate blending. This will result in an increase in the CRU yield of around 50 to 60 thousand b/d.[12] Estimates of planned MTBE capacity additions vary widely between 160,000 b/d and 212,000 b/d by 1995. Oxygenate supply will be further bolstered by investment in the production of other ethers, such as TAME, and capacity creep.[13] In addition to this, planned capacity expansions in alkylation, isomerization and reforming must be taken into

---

12   This calculation assumes current US reformate production at 2.5 mb/d. Decreasing CR severity is assumed to result in a drop in octane quality of 4 (see Tables 3 and 4) and an increase in yield of 4 to 5 per cent. See J. H. Gary, G. E. Handwerk, *Petroleum Refining: Technology and Economics*, Marcel Dekker Inc. 1984 p.87.

13   The 22 captive MTBE plants in the USA have been run at the very low average utilization rate of 63.5 per cent. This leaves considerable scope for increase.

account.[14] In terms of total US supply this means that the volume of US gasoline could increase by 1.2 per cent per annum from 7.3 mb/d in 1990 to around 7.65 mb/d in 1995.

This aggregate analysis of future gasoline supplies ignores relative supplies of the growing number of gasolines with differing specifications. On the one hand, the availability of components for sale as unleaded gasoline has increased greatly and, on the other, supplies of reformulated and oxygenated gasolines will be limited by the scarce supplies of oxygenates and, in the case of reformulated gasoline, by the regulatory cap placed on aromatics content.

(b) Demand. The future demand for motor car fuels will depend first on a multitude of economic and demographic indicators and, secondly, on the new market conditions brought about by green fuel regulations.

The effects of economic growth on motor fuel demand may be countered by increased prices (due to environmental specifications and higher taxes), increased efficiency of the American motor car fleet as a result of the 1990 CAA regulations[15] and the introduction of an alternative fuels programme. Demographic factors, such as size and average age of the population, will also influence overall demand.

The relative demand for motor fuels will depend on the degree of substitutibility, price differentials and, in the case of gasoline, on the effects of both the geographical segregation of markets and the changing content.

Diesel and gasoline fuels are not directly substitutable products. The necessity of buying a new vehicle before being able to take advantage of differences in price between the two fuels is an obstacle to competition. Even so diesel sales do seem to be sensitive to the price differential between gasolines and diesel. The diesel fuel price overtook that of regular unleaded

---

14 'US upgrading, refiners focus on gasoline', *Petroleum Argus*, 5 August 1991, p.4.

15 Corporate Average Fuel Economy is to increase by 40 per cent by the year 2001.

gasoline from 10.79 c/g below in 1980 to 9.25 c/g above in 1990 and during that time diesel sales have slowed from increasing at 5 per cent per annum to remaining level in 1990. Over the next few years diesel is expected to regain its cost advantage versus new gasolines and this may in turn increase diesel's share of the motor fuels market.

With the phasing out of leaded gasoline, the other available brands namely unleaded, oxygenated and reformulated gasolines are directly substitutable. The difference in price between unleaded, oxygenated and reformulated gasolines in adjoining areas or even at the same petrol station complicates the outlook for the relative demand for gasolines. The propensity of consumers to move their custom outside the areas mandated for reformulated gasoline supplies may be further increased by the fact that the majority of affluent Americans live in suburbs on the outskirts of metropolitan areas, thereby, facilitating migration.

However, the Federal or State legislatures may decide to follow the European approach and to increase the taxes on environmentally unfriendly products. This would mean that unleaded gasoline would lose its price advantage relative to new gasolines and that the overall demand for gasoline might be adversely affected.

The changing composition of future gasolines (see Tables 3 and 4) will increase the complexity of forecasting future demand. The addition of oxygenates to green gasolines will increase the octane quality but reduce the calorific content of gasolines. Higher octane may improve engine efficiency[16] thereby minimizing vehicle fuel consumption per mile travelled. The EPA forecastes that higher octane may save up to 43,000 b/d of fuel – almost 25 per cent of the total increase in gasoline demand forecast for 1990–5.[17] This conservation effect will be mitigated or even swamped by the effect on consumption

---

16   The compression ratio of the engine needs to be increased if efficiency is to be improved through using a higher octane gasoline.

17   'New EPA carbon monoxide rules to save up to 43,000 b/d in fuel', *Platt's Oilgram*, 13 September 1990, p.5.

of the lower energy or calorific content of new gasolines.

The EIA has forecast that road diesel consumption will increase by 1.7 per cent per annum on average to 2010, a much lower rate of increase than the average 5 per cent per annum registered between 1979 and 1989.[18] The EIA's long-term forecast for gasoline demand is of a 0.6 per cent increase per annum which implies that overall gasoline demand will increase from 7.3 mb/d in 1990 to 7.5 mb/d in 1995.

(c) Trade. The complex factors that will act on the supply and demand balances in motor fuels markets will affect the oil trade in the USA through the 1990s. In this analysis it is assumed that (1) some refiners will change crude oil feedstock in order to meet more stringent sulphur specifications on oil products, (2) US diesel supplies may only need to be supplemented with minimal imports and (3) America will begin to import gasoline-blending components instead of finished gasoline and may even begin to export other 'dirtier' gasoline-blending components.

High oxygen requirements for new gasolines will lead to some gas for oil substitution and may have the effect of slowing future increases in crude oil imports. The production of MTBE for instance requires methanol and isobutylene feedstocks which will primarily be synthesized from natural gas supplies, methane and butane respectively.

Lower sulphur specifications for diesel, and possibly gasoline (see section 4.3), will put a premium on low sulphur feedstock. It has been estimated that the price differential of low sulphur to high sulphur crudes could increase by as much as $1.50 per barrel, compared to the current difference which ranges between $2.00 and $3.50, if a significant number of refiners use lower sulphur feedstock in order to meet the new regulations instead of investing in increased conversion.[19]

On the other hand, if some refiners decide that the costs of

18   L. Shyu, A. Bohn, 'Effects of the Clean Air Act's highway diesel fuel oil provisions', *Petroleum Supply Monthly*, EIA June 1991.

19   Dr P. McDonald, 'Low-sulphur diesel: the refining industry's next headache?', *Oil Daily Energy Compass*, 27 February 1991.

competing in the highway diesel fuel market[20] are too high and there is some rationalization of US refining capacity, foreign suppliers may be called on. Suppliers such as Canada, Latin America and Europe, may also have a slight cost advantage because of less stringent refinery environmental regulations although this will only serve to negate the extra cost of transport.[21]

The US gasoline trade has assumed great importance over the last decade due to the phasing out of lead in gasoline. The technical solution adopted for the phasing out of lead over the 1980s had the associated affect of reducing the yield of reformate, used in gasoline blending. This factor impaired US refiners' ability to keep US gasoline supplies in pace with the growth in demand and the residual was supplied by Canada, Europe and Latin America. In 1989, the USA imported around 369,000 b/d of finished gasoline and 66,000 b/d of gasoline-blending components, of which 151,000 b/d was European, 47,000 b/d Canadian and 140,000 b/d Latin America. In the same year the USA exported around 39,000 b/d of finished gasoline of which 11,000 b/d went to Mexico. Net imports therefore account for about 5.4 per cent of US gasoline demand of 7.3 mb/d.

The introduction of new types of gasoline in the USA over the next five years will alter US needs. Up to the early 1990s the USA has imported aromatic-rich gasolines for the regular unleaded market. In 1992 and beyond the US will have a surplus of aromatic-rich gasoline blending components but will require ethers, such as MTBE, and good quality paraffinic gasoline blending components, such as isomerate and alkylate.

European and Canadian gasoline producers will be in a good position to supply these new needs, although their position may be compromised by one of two possible factors. Firstly, the need for gasoline imports is likely to increase faster on the west coast

---

20   Refiners may redirect diesel fuel output to non-highway diesel markets which account for over 50 per cent of the total diesel market and are subject to less stringent sulphur specifications.

21   L. Shyu, A. Bohn, op.cit.

leaving European producers at a disadvantage relative to the Far East. Second, if the issue of clean air grows in political importance in Europe then governments will find it increasingly difficult to sanction the export of clean products – especially if refiners need to import cheaper and dirtier gasoline components, most likely from the USA, as a result.

The Far East, on the other hand, seems better placed to supply US needs. First, because if there is rationalization of US refining capacity much of it will be in California where the costs of environmental compliance are so high and which already has trade links with the Far East. Secondly, because the environmental debate has not reached the level of aromatics restrictions or minimum oxygen content, except in Japan. Such restrictions would necessarily impede trade. Thirdly, because large expansions are planned for isomerization and alkylation capacities in this area. According to the *Oil and Gas Journal's* '1990 Worldwide Construction Report' planned isomerization and alkylation expansion in this region accounts for 29 per cent of the world total, and is second only to planned expansion in the USA.[22]

However, the Far East producers are currently experiencing some octane pressure due to lead restrictions and increasing demand and are depending on capacity expansions to maintain gasoline quality and, so, supplies. In this regard European and Canadian gasoline producers will have more flexibility.

---

22 A. Seymour, *The World Refining System and the Oil Products Trade*, pp.10–12.

6 CONCLUSION

For the environmental regulation of industry to be a success two conditions need to be met. In the first instance environmental requirements must be stated clearly to facilitate cost analysis and planning, as was the case with the phasing out of lead in gasoline. Secondly, industry must be reassured that the investments required are of a long-term nature and therefore economically justifiable.

The requirements for reformulated gasoline are the most uncertain and costly of the new motor fuel regulations. At present refiners' horizon stretches only to the production of 'simple' reformulated gasoline in 1995 and even in this case crucial fuel parameters such as aromatics content are as yet unspecified. By 1997 and again by 2000 refiners will have to meet new specifications for reformulated gasoline which will not be known until the Auto/Oil programme is finalized. The costs of these reformulations will depend on how radically the specifications for each differ. Congress has also allowed for the possibility that more than one fuel formulation may be certified as reformulated gasoline, thereby widening the range of possible cost curves.

Time must also be allowed for investment to be planned and implemented. The Clean Air Act has suffered consistently over the past twenty years from unrealistic schedules. The new incarnation of the CAA is no exception. Up to 55 per cent of US gasoline supplies may need to be reformulated three times over the 1990s, for production start-ups in January 1995, 1997 and 2000. To put this into perspective: during the whole of the 1980s refiners managed to convert around 50 per cent of total gasoline sales from leaded to unleaded gasoline.

Despite Congress's stated aim in the 1990 CAAA to employ

'market mechanisms' in order to increase flexibility and to facilitate planning, it has created intensely bureaucratic permitting and monitoring procedures which will inevitably delay implementation. In fact, Congress's area-by-area approach with regard to oxygenated and reformulated gasoline will segregate gasoline markets and put a great deal of stress on the physical infrastructure, thereby reducing flexibility. Also, the provision for tradeable credits has been significantly scaled down subsequent to the 1990 CAAA. Whereas Congress had envisaged tradeable credits in the oxygen, benzene and aromatics contents of reformulated gasoline, the programme has since been scaled down to oxygen only. These inflexibilities will raise prospective costs and impair refiners' ability to meet the requirements in the time schedule allocated.

It is also crucial that US refiners perceive these investments to be profitable if America is to continue to be self-sufficient in oil product supplies. Before the 1990 Clean Air Act Amendments were passed US refiners lived in fear that the downturn in demand precipitated by the high crude prices of the Gulf War and possible increases in oil product taxation would lead to lower utilization rates and, consequently, undermine the upturn in refiner margins in 1988–90. Congress managed to add to this anxiety over a future downturn in demand by mandating costly new gasolines and diesel, alternative fuel programmes and insisting on higher efficiency from motor cars.

Those refiners who do invest are facing significant uncertainties specifically as a result of provisions contained in the 1990 CAAA. Refiners who do invest in new motor fuel supplies may face price competition from cheaper and perfectly substitutable unleaded gasolines either as a result of waivers within the mandated areas or from gasoline stations located on the boundaries of mandated areas. Of course, Congress could reassure refiners by promising increased taxation on 'dirtier' gasolines. However such a commitment has not been made.

The 'command-and-control' approach of the motor fuel regulations is complex and imposes costs which are disproportionate to prospective environmental benefits. The alternative fuel programme signals to refiners that the investments in reformulating gasoline and diesel may have no long-term future. If refinery technology cannot compete with the environmental solutions offered by alternatives, then the future of hydrocarbon motor fuels may be threatened by increasingly desperate legislation. The second condition for the successful implementation of motor fuel regulations has emphatically not been met.

Congress's attempt to address the public's concern over urban pollution, hazardous wastes and acid rain may be described, at best, as a heroic adventure in the face of scientific uncertainty or, at worst, a complete misallocation of resources which will cause both fundamental change and, possibly, irreparable damage to the domestic refining industry. In terms of the environment the enormous impetus to research that the auto/oil regulations will create is likely to outweigh the benefits of the emission reductions that the regulations are seeking to achieve.

ANNEX 1 THE ENVIRONMENTAL IMPACT OF ROAD TRANSPORT EMISSIONS

The environmental problems caused, or added to, by vehicle emissions are more insidious or diverse than those caused by direct inhalation. In fact scientific knowledge of the ways in which we might be affected by these emissions is constantly evolving. The following section describes our current understanding of the impact of transport-related pollutants on our health, economy and aesthetic appreciation of our surroundings.[1] Of most concern are six types of emissions; namely carbon monoxide (CO), particulates, nitrogen oxides (NOx), toxic hydrocarbons, gasoline additives (such as lead) and carbon dioxide (CO_2).

CO is a colourless and odourless gas that is emitted from the tailpipe as a result of incomplete combustion of fuel. The more complete the combustion process the more CO_2 is produced in the place of CO. Compression-ignition engines (which are diesel fuelled) are more efficient than spark-ignition engines (which utilize gasoline) and so emit less CO. CO is a toxic compound that remains in the atmosphere for many months[2] before being oxidized to produce CO_2. CO air concentrations become particularly dangerous in the winter when temperature inversions trap accumulating CO emissions under a stream of warmer air.

CO enters the bloodstream through inhalation and reduces the capability of red blood cells to absorb oxygen. The symptoms

---

1 Respectively, these represent the primary, secondary and tertiary criteria with which the US legislation has justified regulation.

2 The CO will eventually turn to CO_2 see T. E. Graedel, and P. J. Crutzen, 'The changing atmosphere', *Scientific American*, September 1989, p.62.

of this are disco-ordination and lightheadedness.[3] In high enough concentration CO can cause death and to this end car exhaust is used as a means of suicide. However, in lower concentrations CO poses a threat to those with a weak or diseased heart and can permanently damage the unborn foetus. 'The American Lung Association estimates that over 1.4 million pregnant women live in areas which have failed to attain the (EPA) carbon monoxide standards.'[4]

'Particulate matter' is a generic term used to describe all solids that are suspended in the atmosphere. The genre may include anything from ordinary dust particles to the bigger hydrocarbon molecules that go through incomplete combustion and are spewed out in a vehicle's exhaust. Although breathing in all such particles is detrimental to health, some of the hydrocarbon or sulphate particles can cause severe damage. Ordinary particulates also provide a surface for other volatile organic compounds (such as benzo(a)pyrene, a human carcinogen) to be absorbed and this makes inhalation much more serious. Also attachment to the particle prolongs the atmospheric life of VOCs and, therefore, increases their chance of being inhaled. Particulate as well as CO airborne concentrations are influenced by the seasons. In the case of particulates, rain decreases the concentration of suspended particles.[5]

Diesel combustion results in greater particulate emissions from the exhaust than gasoline[6] because the former fuel contains more sulphur and heavier hydrocarbon compounds,

---

3   Organization for Economic Co-operation and Development (OECD), *Transport and the Environment*, OECD, 1988, p.49.

4   *Senate Report No. 101–228*, 'Clean Air Act, Amendments', 27 October 1990, p.7.

5   P. R. Portney, 'Air Pollution Policy' in Portney (ed.), *Public Policies for Environmental Protection*, Resources for the Future, 1990, fn. 17 pp.92–3.

6   Although gasoline is more volatile than diesel and therefore use of the former will result in greater evaporation of toxic unburned hydrocarbon particles. See below.

both of which burn with great difficulty.[7] However, 'diesel driven vehicles also have better combustion efficiencies, therefore emitting lower rates of HC and CO, and they emit fewer NOx (on an uncontrolled basis) due to lower ignition temperatures.'[8]

These particles not only soil building surfaces and decrease visibility but also and more importantly they can be breathed in and cause serious damage to one's health. Smaller particles penetrate further into the lungs and damage delicate tissues. This knowledge has evolved over the last 20 years and so legislation now targets only those particles under 10 microns in diameter (PM-10) instead of all suspended particles (as was the case in 1970).[9] PM-10 from vehicle exhaust not only damage the lungs but are thought to be responsible for approximately 860 cancer cases every year in the USA.[10]

NOx emissions from vehicles indirectly add to the problem of particulate concentrations and, so, NOx gases are also known as particulate precursors. In the atmosphere these gases (most especially nitrogen dioxide (NO_2)) can react with the hydroxyl radical (OH) to form nitric acid (HNO_3) and then undergo further transformation into nitrate (NO_{3-}) particles.[11] However, more lethal than these nitrates is the effect of breathing in toxic metals particles dissolved in suspended acidic liquids, such as nitric acid or dissolved nitrates. This cocktail is more dangerous if sulphuric acid, instead of nitric acid, provides the medium for the metal solution as sulphur dioxide becomes more acidic in the atmosphere. One study estimates that the

---

7   Also catalytic converters that trap the majority of particulates in the exhaust are not efficient for diesel-run vehicles as the device is intolerant of the sulphur content of the fuel.

8   OECD, op.cit., p.47.

9   This has meant past information gleaned from the monitoring of airborne particulate concentration is now less relevant.

10   *Senate Report No. 101–228*, 'Clean Air Act, Amendments', 27 October 1990, p.8.

11   W. Harrington, *Acid Rain: Science and Policy, A Primer*, Resources for the Future, 1989, p.2.

combination of these two types of acidic/metallic cocktails account for 2 per cent of US mortalities, some 50,000 deaths per annum.[12] In Mexico City the problem is so severe that inhabitants complain of a continual metallic taste in the mouth.

NOx emissions directly and indirectly affect our lives and environment in many other ways. Directly, inhalation of NOx, especially NO_2, can cause or aggravate respiratory disorders. Also, NO_2 has a brownish tinge that effects visibility and if it comes in contact with the ground it can damage vegetation. This dry precipitation is the less well-known form of acid rain, or, as it is more accurately described acid deposition.

Acid deposition encompasses two processes. Acid rain, or wet deposition, is the process by which SO_2 and NOx emissions that form acids and their salts in the atmosphere are deposited through precipitation. Dry deposition describes the ways in which these gases 'are taken up directly by plants or are oxidized and become acid sulfates and nitrates on the ground'.[13] SO_2 is considered the greater evil as it is capable of retaining 45 per cent more acidity (on an equivalent weight basis) after oxidization than the NOx gases.[14] Also, the deposition of nitrogen-based compounds, especially nitrates, is good for vegetation whereas any sulphur-based compounds are harmful.[15]

Acid deposition can affect both the ecosystem and human health. Deforestation and dying lakes, most prevalent in the northeastern USA, have often been identified as the result of increased acid deposition. The evidence available for this is stronger in the case of lakes than for treelife. Firstly because aquatic life is much more susceptible to a decrease in pH

---

12 H. F. French, *Clearing the Air: A Global Agenda*, Worldwatch Paper 94, January 1990, p.12.

13 W. Harrington, op.cit., p.2.

14 Ibid., p.9.

15 *Senate Report No. 101–228*, 'Clean Air Act, Amendments', 27 October 1990, p.262.

levels[16] and second because it is difficult to separate the severe effect of ground-level ozone on vegetation (see below) from that of acid deposition.[17] Increased pH levels of lakes in affected areas vary with the seasons. They are especially high when the snow melts and during the rainy season.[18] Acid deposition can cause damage to health by releasing toxic metals, such as aluminium from the soil and lead from waterpipes, into the water supply and food chain.[19] Corrosion of buildings is another result of acid deposition.

Whereas the contribution of NOx emissions to acid deposition is partial, its contribution to ground-level ozone formation is central. At ground level ozone is formed through the interaction of NOx with Volatile Organic Compounds (VOCs)[20], both emitted in vehicle exhaust, in the presence of sunlight. As the reaction is a photochemical one, ozone only accumulates in high concentrations during periods of sustained sunshine. Like acid rain the process of ozone formation is a complex one which has not been fully understood. For instance, one complexity is that nitric oxide will serve to degrade ozone near the emission source, whereas if the same gas is carried further downwind it can contribute to ozone formation.[21] Also, the long distances acidic gases may be carried before being

---

16 'The measure of the acidity or alkalinity of an aqueous solution on a scale running from 1 to 14 with 7 being neutral. Numbers less than seven indicate increasing acidity...' P. Brackley, *Energy and Environmental Terms: A Glossary*, Royal Institute of International Affairs and Policy Studies Institute, 1989, p.118.

17 Ibid., pp.7–8.

18 Swedish National Environmental Protection Board, *Acidification and Air Pollution: A Brief Guide*, Second edition, p.31.

19 Ibid., p.6.

20 The term Volatile Organic Compound is often used as a substitute for unburned hydrocarbons 'since some organic compounds being emitted may contain elements in addition to hydrogen and carbon.' See P. Brackley, op.cit, pp.166–7.

21 *Senate Report No. 101–228*, 'Clean Air Act, Amendments', 27 October 1990, pp.48–9.

deposited makes it difficult to identify the emission source or to regulate that source.

High in the stratosphere ozone protects us by filtering out the more harmful rays of the sun. However, ground-level ozone serves no such purpose and, like other oxidants, is toxic. The effects of ozone are similar to that of smoking.[22] It can cause lung and eye irritation and decrease the resistance of the immune system. Ozone also reduces visibility and causes severe damage to vegetation. The EPA estimates that ozone costs between \$2 and \$3 billion a year in crop losses,[23] while the Congressional Research Service estimates a high of \$4.3 billion not including long-term damage to the genetic base of high-yielding crops.[24]

Unburned hydrocarbon emissions from fuel evaporation (gasoline is more volatile than diesel and therefore results in greater evaporative losses) not only act as an ozone precursor but also constitute toxic gases in their own right. The 'toxic effects may include carcinogenity, reproductive problems, neurotoxicity and chronic organ toxicity (for example liver disease)'.[25] Of the hydrocarbon compounds aromatics[26] pose the greatest health hazard although olefins[27] are also considered dangerous. The aromatic benzene, or derivatives such as benzo(a)pyrene, is a listed carcinogen and has been linked to leukaemia incidence.[28] Many of the other aromatics are

---

22 Because of the similarity of the effects of ozone and smoking it is difficult to estimate the effects of ozone in isolation especially as the impact of ozone is decreasing relative to smoking.

23 *Senate Report No. 101–228*, 'Clean Air Act, Amendments', 27 October 1990, p.8.

24 OECD, op.cit, p.52.

25 M. Shapiro, 'Toxic Substances Policy' in Portney (ed.), op.cit, p.196.

26 The group of hydrocarbons with six carbon atoms.

27 Like aromatics olefins contain a double bond that make them unstable and, so, reactive. The olefin family, otherwise known as alkenes, are characterized by the formula $CnH2n$.

28 OECD, op.cit, p.50.

considered procarcinogen.[29]

Other listed hazardous air pollutants include two gasoline additives, namely lead and Methyl-Tertiary-Butylether (MTBE). Lead is certainly the most popularized environmental evil in the petrol tank, even to the extent that most of the others have been ignored. Lead is known to accumulate in bone and other tissues[30] and to have adverse affects on the nervous system, circulation, kidneys and reproductive system which can result in hypertension, heart attack, strokes and death. In addition it is thought to be carcinogenic.[31] It also causes irreversible damage to the learning ability of children and according to one estimate destroys '3 to 4 IQ points on average for the 2 percent of children with blood levels above 30 micrograms per deciliter'.[32]

To a large extent lead was substituted by increasing the aromatic content of gasoline and adding other additives such as MTBE. Aromatics we have already identified as highly unstable compounds and potentially carcinogenic. MTBE is also proving to have its own environmental drawbacks. Not only is MTBE a fire hazard but in its raw state it emits toxic peroxide fumes. Further tests are currently being carried out by the EPA to ascertain if MTBE combustion produces other hazardous emissions.[33]

The most controversial of the acclaimed environmental phenomena of today is the 'greenhouse effect'. It is generally thought, although far from proven, that the earth's temperature is increasing as a result of the build up of so-called 'greenhouse gases'. These gases (CO_2, methane, nitrous oxide, ozone and chlorofluorocarbons to name but a few), like clouds at

---

29 Procarcinogenic compounds only become active carcinogens through the metabolic process.

30 H. F. French, op.cit, p.14.

31 *Senate Report No. 101–228*, 'Clean Air Act, Amendments', 27 October 1990, p.113.

32 Ibid.

33 *Senate Report No. 101–228*, 'Clean Air Act, Amendments', 27 October 1990, p.117.

night, absorb the sun's radiation as it is reflected by the earth and, so, their accumulation in the atmosphere primarily as a result of fossil fuel combustion is deemed to have a net effect on worldwide temperature. The problem scientists face is, firstly, establishing that worldwide temperatures are on an increasing trend when climate is inherently erratic on a regional basis; second, establishing that this trend is greater than can be explained by the cyclical nature of the earth's temperature and, third, proving that the accumulation of trace elements in the atmosphere is causing the phenomenon.

CO_2 is the most plentiful of the greenhouse gases and, therefore, the focus of regulation. CO_2 is also a stable gas and may remain unchanged in the atmosphere for around 100 years.[34] To reverse, or even stabilize, the accumulation of CO_2 will require global awareness and an immense diversion of resources into energy efficiency. Both are tall orders but according to many scientists the stakes could not be higher. The primary fear is that increasing temperatures, by melting the polar icecaps, will result in a rising sea level and a reduction of the earth's land surface.

---

34 T. E. Graedel and P. J. Crutzen, op.cit, p.62.

ANNEX 2   THE CLEAN AIR ACT

A2.1 A Legislative History of the CAA

Although Public Law 159, the basis of the CAA, was first passed by Congress on 14 July 1955,[1] most commentators refer to the 1970 CAA. In fact major amendments of the CAA have been made in 1963, 1970, 1977 and now in 1990 (see Table 3). However, the 1970 amendments endowed a federal institution (the Environmental Protection Agency (EPA)) with the responsibility of setting and ensuring National Ambient Air Quality Standards (NAAQS). This was a clear break with Congress's traditional policy which had been to remain in an advisory position.[2]

(a) Objectives of the CAA. In 1971 the EPA set NAAQS for five pollutants namely CO, SO_2, NOx, oxidants and hydrocarbons.[3] The central purpose of the NAAQS was to protect the US public from any adverse effects on their health of breathing in the surrounding air. The NAAQS was meant to constitute an upper limit for the concentration of certain airborne pollutants and this limit was to be set sufficiently below the danger threshold[4]

---

1   *Senate Report No.101–228*, Minority views of Senator Symms, p.419.

2   The 1965 Motor Vehicle Air Pollution Act only invited the HEW to set emission specifications for manafacturers. See P. R. Portney, 'Air Pollution Policy' in Portney (ed.), *Public Policies for Environmental Protection*, Resources for the Future, 1990, p.30.

3   Study Group administered by Resources for the Future (Hans. H. Landsberg – Chairman), *Energy: The Next Twenty Years*, The Ford Foundation, 1979, p.374.

to provide an 'adequate margin of safety'.[5]

Besides health, two lesser standards based on secondary and tertiary[6] criteria were adopted by Congress. The second criteria was economic. The primary health-based standard had also to ensure the protection of national resources, such as buildings or agriculture, from degradation. Only in the case of sulphur dioxide, however, was a more stringent secondary standard promulgated. The third criteria was aesthetic, meaning that the previous standards had also to be adequate to protect visibility in US national parks and wildernesses.

The NAAQS have not remained static since the early 1970s. The EPA was given a short period of time by Congress to set the five NAAQS subsequent to the 1970 legislation. As a result the 1971 NAAQS were not based on a sufficient or conclusive body of evidence.[7] This was recognized by Congress in the 1977 CAA amendments which established a five-yearly review of the NAAQS in order to promote research and flexibility. Subsequent to 1971 new NAAQS were established for total suspended particulates and lead and the NAAQS for hydrocarbons was dropped in 1983. Also, the EPA narrowed their definitions of oxidants, particulates and NOx to target particular subsections of those groups, namely ozone, PM–10[8] and NO_2 respectively.[9] At present there are six NAAQS for ozone, PM–10, lead, SO_2, NO_2 and CO although the EPA have not yet concluded their most recent five-yearly review for SO_2, lead or ozone.[10]

---

4   A concept based on the premise that low concentrations are not harmful to health. See ibid., p.32.

5   *Senate report No.101–228*, p.5.

6   The tertiary criteria was adopted in the Congressional amendments of 1977.

7   'The original standard for carbon monoxide, for instance, was based on a single study involving 12 people.' W. D. Ruckleshaus, 'Risk, Science and Democracy' in T. S. Glickman, M. Gough, (eds), *Readings in Risk*, Resources for the Future, 1990, p.107.

8   All those particles under 10 microns in diameter.

9   *Senate Report No.101–228*, p.9.

10 Ibid., p.6.

The NAAQS divide the USA into areas of attainment and nonattainment. Each pollutant is assigned a standard involving a one-hourly, eight-hourly or twentyfour-hourly air concentration mean. An area is deemed nonattainment if its standard mean is violated more than once a year, or, in the case of ozone, three times in each three year period.[11]

There are two related drawbacks to this approach. The first is that the NAAQS does not prevent the inter-US migration of pollution sources from nonattainment to attainment Air Quality Control Region (AQCR). In this way the NAAQS may serve only to redistribute pollution within the USA rather than to decrease US emissions. The second is that air pollutants cannot be confined within an AQCR. Therefore, an AQCR that contributes to another AQCR's nonattainment cannot be penalized. Furthermore the nonattainment AQCR would be unfairly penalized with little or no benefit in air quality.

To prevent inter-US migration of pollution sources three categories of attainment or Prevention of Significant Deterioration (PSD) areas were established in the 1977 amendments. The most stringent category was that for national parks and wildernesses which specified an allowable maximum much lower than that of the NAAQS. The second category sought to maintain cleaner areas and established a maximum standard slightly lower than that of the NAAQS; and the third was established for those borderline attainment areas whose air quality was bound by the NAAQS. However, the PSD classification still did not tackle the problems caused by pollutant sources that contributed to the nonattainment of another AQCR.

The 1990 amendments redefined nonattainment. Any AQCR that contributes to the violation of NAAQS in whichever region is now classified as nonattainment. In Title I of the 1990 amendments twelve states have been classified as an ozone transport region which means each will be treated as a nonattainment state until all of the area has attained its ozone NAAQS. Exemptions are also made for those nonattainment

11 P. R. Portney (ed.), op.cit, p.44.

states that can show that emission reductions will not serve to achieve attainment and may even result in a deterioration in air quality.[12]

(b) Means employed by the CAA. Although Congress was willing to sanction the setting of federal standards it was not keen to ignore state boundaries in implementing them. In 1970 the task of implementation was neatly divided between the EPA and the states. The states were given the task of achieving the NAAQS through plant-by-plant emission reductions and the EPA was to supervise this process as well as setting standards for new emission sources that would serve to maintain the NAAQS once they had been achieved. Portney suggests that this division of labour was sensitive to political factors, in that if the EPA were to directly regulate existing plants then accusations of favouritism might be made.[13] In practice, however, this has not cushioned the EPA from charges that it has unfairly targeted some industries rather than others (the debate between the automobile and oil industries is an example) or that it has unfairly exempted some states[14] from certain of the CAA provisions.

Since 1970 the EPA has set standards for all new and modified stationary sources and all new automotive vehicles. The New Source Performance Standards (NSPS) for plants were to ensure that all new or modified sources installed the best emission control technology available. Since then a confusing array of terms have been used to categorize these technology requirements[15] according to the status of the AQCR. However, the principle has remained the same.

---

12   In some instances NOx emissions, which are ozone precursors, may serve to scavange ozone near the emission source; see Chapter 2.

13   P. R. Portney, 'Air Pollution Policies' in Portney (ed.), op.cit., p.39.

14   See 'Hermetically sealed law', *Wall Street Journal*, 15 December 1989 cited in the *Senate Report No.101–228*, Minority view of Senator Symms, p.475.

15   Lowest Available Emissions Rate, Best Available Control Technology, Maximum Available Control Technology among others.

The task of bringing AQCR into attainment was left to the states with the EPA in the role of supervisor. The State Implementation Plan (SIP) was to require the EPA's approval and as a final sanction the EPA was directed to impose a Federal Implementation Plan (FIP). The SIP was to contain details of air quality monitoring, an inventory of emissions, a timetable for emissions reduction on a plant-by-plant basis and the proposed impact that the emission reductions would have on air quality. No new or modified source was to be allowed to operate in a nonattainment region subsequent to the submission of the SIP unless the increase in emissions was offset by an equivalent decrease from a source located in the same AQCR.

As the attainment deadlines set by the EPA for 1975, 1982 and 1987 came and went the problems of the SIP became evident. Lack of resources, time, data and political will all conspired in the failure of the SIPs.[16] Lack of resources and time exacerbated the problem of insufficient and inaccurate data. The states relied wholly on the submission of inventories from the sources themselves to estimate emissions. Furthermore the models on which the states based the impact of the proposed emission reduction on air quality were over-simplistic and, in any case, the monitoring information was insufficient to accurately assess pollutant air concentrations. Lack of political will was also a potent factor and often born out, not of sheer self-interest but of sincere unease over federal and state policy. The SIPs, or the Federal Implementation Plan (FIP) were seen from many quarters as either inappropriate to the environmental problems in hand, overly harsh or even unfeasible.

The 1990 amendments have attempted to address all these

---

16   For Congress's view of the reasons for the CAA's failure see Senate Report; for the EPA's see W. D. Rucklehaus, 'Risk, Science and Democracy' in T. S. Glickman and M. Gough (eds), op.cit., for an independent assessment see P. R. Portney, 'Air Pollution Policy' in Portney (ed), op.cit. and for a case study of Ohio see M. Steinman, *Energy and Environmental Issues*, D.C.Heath and Co., 1979, chapter 7.

problems. From a scientific perspective Congress has emphasized more realistic deadlines, continued research into the formation and health impact of pollution, improvements in the monitoring of emissions and air quality and improvement in the techniques used to model the emissions/air quality relationship. Charges of squandering public funds or unfairness are to be countered through Congress's market-led approach. The use of permits, credits and marketable allowances are meant to achieve emissions reduction at the lowest possible cost and with the least possible disruption to industry. The role of the offset requirement has been expanded to be used as a sanction against non-implementation of a SIP.

In terms of motivating political will Congress has issued detailed policy guidelines for each category of SIP. This facilitates implementation in that each SIP will have to justify the adoption of an alternative policy in terms of equivalent or greater emission reduction and that in the event of non-compliance an FIP could be drawn up much more quickly. Congress has also increased the criminal liability of any individual involved in the falsifying of an SIP or permit from a misdemenour to a felony.

In 1977 the distinct roles of the EPA and the state started to blur as Congress tackled the complex problem of automotive pollution. It was realized that the EPA's standards for new or modified stationary and mobile sources introduced an incentive for industry and automobile owners not to improve or replace their existing plants or vehicles, thereby resulting in increased emissions. To counter this effect on automotive pollution vehicle inspection programmes and traffic control measures were recommended. Since then Congress has been more forthright in mandating policies that affect existing mobile and stationary sources not only nationwide but also targeting particular states. The 1990 amendments has not only constricted the states' room for manoeuvre but has also given the EPA a much bigger stick to encourage them with.

A2.2 The Main Provisions of the 1990 Amendments

Title I: *Provisions for Attainment and Maintenance of NAAQS*

'Nonattainment'[17] is redefined in accordance with further understanding of the behaviour of airborne pollution. First, an area may be deemed non-attainment if it contributes to the violation of NAAQS[18] in another region. Secondly, nonattainment now includes many subcategories, for instance moderate or severe, which determine the number of years allowable for a nonattainment region to achieve the NAAQS.

Title I also provides a sounder factual basis for the SIP[19] by issuing federal guidelines for better air quality monitoring and modelling (see Title IX). The sanction for non-implementation of a SIP will be withdrawal of federal highway grants (excepting safety-related projects) and an emission offset requirement (see Title V) of an additional 100 per cent.

To reduce ozone each nonattainment state is required to reduce VOC emissions 15 per cent by end-1996 and 3 per cent each successive year until it achieves the NAAQS. The EPA[20] is

---

17 The Clean Air Act (CAA) divides the USA into various air quality control regions. The air quality of each of these regions is monitored in order to determine the air concentration of specific pollutants designated by Congress. A maximum air concentration level is established for each pollutant known as the National Ambient Air Quality Standard (NAAQS), involving a one-hourly, eight-hourly or twenty-four hourly air concentration mean. An area is deemed 'nonattainment' if the standard mean for any of the specified pollutants is violated more than once a year or, in the case of ozone, three times in each three year period. At present there are six NAAQS established for PM–10 (particles under 10 microns in diameter), ozone, lead, sulphur dioxide, nitrogen dioxide and carbon monoxide.

18 See above footnote.

19 A State Implementation Plan (SIP) is required from each nonattainment state showing, through the use of scientific modelling techniques, that their proposed emission reductions will achieve the NAAQS by the relevant date.

also to regulate the use of paints and solvents in order to reduce emissions. All CO nonattainment areas have attainment deadlines either in December 1995 or December 2000. PM–10 nonattainment areas must attain their NAAQS by either December 1994 or December 2001. Other areas in violation of the NAAQS will have to attain by November 1995.

Title II: *Provisions Relating to Mobile Sources*

Title II details some of the transportation-related policies mandated for nonattainment areas in Title I. (a) The specifications for all US automotive fuel supplies have been redefined. Gasoline will contain detergents to reduce engine deposits by 1995 and the sulphur content of road diesel will be reduced 80 per cent by October 1993. Reformulated gasoline and an alternative fuel programme are to be introduced in nine cities to reduce ozone, carbon monoxide and benzene pollutants. Oxygenated gasoline will be introduced by November 1992 in serious CO nonattainment areas. (b) New standards reducing NHMC[21] vehicle emissions by 39 per cent and cutting NOx[22] emissions by 60 per cent are to be phased in between model years 1994 and 1996. A new tailpipe standard for CO emissions from vehicles starting the engine at 20 degrees fahrenheit (known as 'cold start', has been established for all new vehicles. (d) All vehicles manufactured after 1993 are to have emission control diagnostic systems which will alter engine conditions to minimize emissions. The system will also be able to determine whether it has been tampered with or if the vehicle has been misfuelled. The system's ability will aid a programme for more stringent yearly vehicle inspection and maintenance. (e) A research programme is established to investigate the health impact of current and proposed gasoline

---

20   The Environmental Protection Agency (EPA) is responsible to Congress for the administration of environmental regulations.

21   Any Volatile Organic Compound (VOC) larger than methane which is the smallest of VOCs and nonreactive, therefore, it will not contribute to ozone formation.

additives and the health impact of vehicle emissions of benzene, formaldehyde (from methanol fuelled vehicles) and 1,3 butadiene.

Title III: *Hazardous Air Pollutants*

This title revises section 112 of the CAA and aims to reduce the 'incidence of cancer attributable to exposure to hazardous air pollutants emitted by stationary sources of not less 75 per centum'.

In phases between October 1992 and October 2000 the installation of state-of-the-art pollution control technologies will be made mandatory for 189 listed hazardous air pollutant source categories. Any member of the public may petition the EPA to add to or remove a substance from the list of hazardous pollutants. Also a Chemical Safety and Investigation Board will be established to monitor accidents, assess the risks posed by certain plants and to analyse safety procedures. In addition accident prevention regulations will be issued covering the use of 189 listed pollutants.

The MACT provisions for HAPs require that each of the source categories and sub-categories achieve 'the average emission limitation achieved by the best performing 12 percent of the existing sources (for which the Administrator has emissions information)'.[23] However, the collection of emissions data to identify sources and the division of category, and, more especially, sub-category sources has been left to the EPA to complete by October 1991.

Title IV: *Acid Deposition Control*

'The purpose of this title is to reduce the adverse effects of acid deposition through reductions in annual emissions of sulphur dioxide of ten million tons...and...of nitrogen oxides emissions

---

22   The other component of the ozone reaction.

23   The Clean Air Act Amendments, 1990, Title III, Section 301 (d)(3)(A).

of approximately two million tons from 1980 emissions levels (effective by 2000)'.

Annual (credits are not transferable between years) emission allowances are allocated to each utility and may be freely traded between utilities. An allowance bonus may be awarded if the required emissions reductions are achieved through the use of conservation technology.

Title V: *Permits*

All 'major' stationary sources or 'affected' sources listed in Titles I to III must enter a permit scheme. Like the SIP, the permit must detail all operations, emissions and planned changes for emission reductions. Any change in operation, increase in emissions or alteration to planned investments must first receive sanction from the relevant authority. The EPA may oversee or overrule any state sanction.

For every modification or new construction that results in an increase in emissions the utility must secure a reduction in emissions from another utility in the same nonattainment area in excess of its own increase. Depending on which category a nonattainment area is classified under there will be an appropriate offset requirement ranging from 10 to 100 per cent additional emission reduction.

The permit must also specify the fee to be paid by each source. The fee will cover the cost of enforcing the terms of the permit including areas such as research, monitoring air quality, inventories, air quality modelling demonstrations and producing regulations and guidelines.

Title VI: *Stratospheric Ozone Protection*

In order to protect the stratospheric ozone layer and to reduce greenhouse gases Congress has planned to phase out the production of chlorofluorocarbons in two stages. Class I substances will be phased out by 1 January 2000 and production of class II substances will cease by 1 January 2015.

Title VII: *Provisions Relating to Enforcement*

The enforcement title allows for an increased range of civil and criminal punishments to penalize violations of any provisions of the SIP or permit programme. Criminal proceedings may result in a large fine, up to five years in prison or both.

Title VIII: *Miscellaneous Provisions*

Section 821 of the amended CAA mandates that each source in the permit programme must submit an inventory of its CO_2. This is intended to facilitate a CO_2 emissions reduction programme if it proves necessary and to aid research by making its information publicly available.

Title IX: *Clean Air Research*

The research programme will include (a) a study in methods of air quality monitoring, air quality modelling and preparation of emission inventories (b) a study of 'the short-term and long-term effects of air pollutants' from wood smoke to hazardous substances (c) 'a basic engineering research and technology program to develop, evaluate, and demonstrate nonregulatory strategies and technologies for air pollution prevention' (d) the continuance of the National Acid Precipitation Assessment Program which first started in 1980.

OIES PUBLICATIONS

Books

OIES 1   *The Market for North Sea Crude Oil* by R. Mabro, R. Bacon, M. Chadwick, M. Halliwell & D. Long, 1986. UK £29.50; Overseas £33.

OIES 2   *Natural Gas: An International Perspective* by R. Mabro ed., 1986. UK £19.50; Overseas £21.50.

OIES 3   *OPEC & the World Oil Market* by R. Mabro ed., 1986. UK £25; Overseas £28.

OIES 4   *Soviet Oil Exports* by M. Chadwick, D. Long & M. Nissanke, 1987. UK £29.50; Overseas £33

OIES 5   *The 1986 Oil Price Crisis* by R. Mabro ed., 1988. UK £25; Overseas £28

OIES 6   *Natural Gas: Governments & Oil Companies in the Third World* by A. Davison, C. Hurst & R. Mabro, 1988. UK £25; Overseas £28

OIES 7   *Paul Frankel: Common Carrier of Common Sense* by I. Skeet ed., 1989. UK £25; Overseas £28

OIES 8   *Demand, Prices & the Refining Industry* by R. Bacon, M. Chadwick, J. Dargay, D. Long & R. Mabro, 1990. UK £29.50; Overseas £33

OIES 9   *The Economics of Natural Gas: Pricing, Planning & Policy* by D. Julius & A. Mashayekhi, 1990. UK £25; Overseas £28

Special Papers

SP1   *The First Oil War* by R. Mabro ed., 1990. UK and Overseas: £195

SP2   *A Dialogue Between Oil Producers and Consumers: The Why and the How* by R. Mabro, 1991. UK and Overseas: £150.

Review Series

Energy Economics

EE7   *An Econometric Analysis of Exploration & Extraction of Oil on the UK Continental Shelf* by M. Hashem Pesaran, 1989

EE8   *Empirical Modelling of Canadian Petroleum Exploration Activity* by C.M. Desbarats, 1989

EE9   *Have Low Oil Prices Reversed the Decline in Energy Demand? A Case-Study for the UK* by J. M. Dargay, 1990

EE10   *Rockets & Feathers: The Asymmetric Speed of Adjustment of UK Retail Gasoline Prices to Cost Changes by* R. Bacon, 1990

EE11   *Dynamic Modelling and Testing of OPEC Behaviour* by Carol Dahl and Mine Yucel, 1990

EE12   *Taxation and the Optimization of Oil Exploration and Production: The UK Continental Shelf* by Carlo A. Favero, 1990

EE13   *The Irreversible Demand Effects of High Oil Prices. Motor Fuels in France, Germany and the UK* by J. M. Dargay, 1991

EE14   *Speed of Adjustment and Market Structure: A Study of the Gasoline Market in Germany* by Alessandro Lanza, 1991

EE15   *Oil Investments in the North Sea* by Carlo A. Favero & M. Hashem Pesaran, 1991

Energy & the Environment

EV1   *Fossil Fuel Consumption & the Environment* by A.M. Davison, 1989

EV2   *Economic Models of Optimal Energy Use under Global Environmental Constraints* by H. W. Gottinger, 1990

EV3   *Policy Models of Long-run Growth under Global Environmental Constraints* by H. W. Gottinger, 1991

EV4   *Energy - Economy - Environmental Models with Special Reference to CO_2 Emission Control* by H. W. Gottinger, 1991